THE TYRANNY
OF NOISE
Robert Alex Baron

You suffer from noise. You wince at the sounds of jackhammers and air compressors. The crash of garbage cans on a Saturday morning stirs you to rage. You curse the sound of a blaring horn. You dread the coming of the sonic boom.

You are not alone.

Millions throughout the world suffer the tyranny of noise. In this devastating exposé of a problem that industry and government have refused to recognize, Robert Alex Baron, America's leading authority on noise abatement, reveals the facts others ignore. He tells why doctors consider noise to be a contributing cause of diseases ranging from headaches to heart attacks. He documents the millions of dollars in compensation owed to sufferers of noise-induced hearing loss, the devaluation of real estate in noisy areas, the accidents and loss of productivity caused by noise. He describes in detail the many, often unnoticed ways in which noise intrudes in our lives, making privacy a meaningless word.

Equally important, the author puts the blame for this colossal din where it belongs: on the corporations and public officials whose greed and indifference have brought acoustic anarchy to our world. He makes concrete, feasible proposals for noise control, challenging the noisemakers to respond. If they do not, he warns, the public will take matters into its own hands. Read this book to find what you can do to turn back the most prevalent polluti

ROBERT ALEX BARON was awakened one morning in 1964 by the ear-shattering cacophony of subway construction in the street below his Manhattan apartment. In a sense he hasn't slept since. Giving up a career as a successful theater manager, he has devoted his time to learning all he can about noise and its control, and passing the information on to others. Head of a leading anti-noise organization, Citizens for a Quieter City, he has appeared as an expert witness before Congressional committees and has given lectures on noise control throughout Europe and the United States.

THE TYRANNY OF NOISE

The
TYRANNY
Of
NOISE

ROBERT ALEX BARON

ST. MARTIN'S PRESS

TD
892
.B37
1970

TO MY WIFE JOAN

Acknowledgments

It would be difficult to list and thank the many people who lent me encouragement and from whom I have learned so much through informal conversations, conference discussions, and writings—published and unpublished.

I must begin by thanking John Wharton for his foresight and encouragement. His support and guidance first made it possible for me to work toward the goal of noise abatement.

Further thanks go to Jerome Nathanson and the other members of the Board of Directors of Citizens for a Quieter City, and to the steering committee of the Upper Sixth Avenue Noise Abatement Association. I am especially indebted to Dr. Samuel Rosen, who generously gave me of his time and wisdom, and Martin Hirschorn and Francis Kirschner, who not only shared noise control expertise but encouraged my search for abatement.

Among the noise control specialists I also thank James Botsford, John Duda, Alfred Greenberg, and Dr. Alexander Cohen and Herb Jones of the Public Health Service. Acoustician Lew Goodfriend kindly permitted me to quote from *Sound and Vibration* and made available several of his provocative unpublished papers.

I shall always appreciate my all too brief association with the late ecologist Dr. William Vogt, who aptly phrased the problem as "not mufflers, but the abusive use of technology."

Among the leaders of the international noise abatement movement, I wish to thank John Connell of The Noise Abatement Society, England, and Dr. O. Schenker-Sprüngli, General Secretary of the International Association Against Noise. I am grateful for the cooperation and continued support of the Honorable John V. Lindsay, first as a Congressman and now as Mayor of New York City; the encouragement of the Honorable Percy E. Sutton, President of the Borough of Manhattan; and a special thanks to the Honorable Theodore R. Kupferman, one of the first political figures to recognize—and act on—the validity of my position against excessive urban noise.

Among the many others who provided assistance are Ralph Brozan, Andrew Anspach, Neil Anderson, Wallace Fulton, Dr. Betty Goessel, Dr. Jack Goldman, Irwin Margaloff, Roberta Pryor, Dr. Richard Sullivan, the late Irwin Solomon, and Dr. Bruce Welch. I am especially indebted to James Larkin, and the executives and staff of Scali, McCabe, Sloves, Inc.

I am indebted to Ellie Kurtz for her exceptionally helpful editing of the manuscript.

I accept full responsibility for any errors in fact. The viewpoints I express are my responsibility and do not necessarily represent those of any organization with which I am associated.

Finally, I owe much to my family: to my mother, who taught me to be curious, to my father, who trained me to be persistent. It all may have started with my daughter Stacey, who at the age of two asked me to "stop the noisy street." And this book could never have been completed without the help of my devoted wife Joan, who in some ways bore more of its burden than did the author.

CONTENTS

Prologue To Decibels

Prologue To Decibels

It was 6:00 A.M. on a balmy April day in 1964. The place was a six-block stretch of Manhattan's Sixth Avenue between Radio City Music Hall and Central Park, in the heart of New York City. Thousands of New Yorkers and transients slept in the cosmopolitan neighborhood of apartments, hotels, and schools.

Darkened windows of the apartment houses and the giant buildings owned by CBS, the J.C. Penney Co., and the Equitable Life Assurance Society looked down on a fever of activity in the street. "Slattery's Army" was moving into position, a position it was to hold for three years, from 1964 to 1967. It was a highly mechanized contractor's army, equipped with eighty-pound-class pneumatic paving-breakers, track-mounted high-impact rock drills, giant cranes and bulldozers. Its pneumatic tools were powered by a battery of five portable air compressors, each with a normal discharge pressure of one hundred pounds per square inch and a full-load speed of 1,750 rpm. The compressor engines

3

were noisy, six-cylinder diesels of 900 cubic feet per minute (cfm) capacity.

Workers with scarred eardrums were preparing to launch an open-cut subway extension project for the New York City Transit Authority. As luck would have it, the Slattery Construction Company had chosen the southwest corner of Fifty-fifth Street and Sixth Avenue, just opposite the windows of my apartment, to assemble the five compressors.

We apartment-dwellers slept on, unaware that in a few minutes the life of our community would become both a waking and a sleeping nightmare.

The operating engineer started the battery of air compressors. Jackhammer and rock drill operators hunched forward, waiting for the compressed air to feed their vibrating pneumatic tools.

Suddenly, all hell broke loose. What someone later termed "a symphony of insanity" had begun. The overture to a three-year concert combined the sounds of air compressors, jackhammers, rock drills, chain saws, and dynamite blasts, with additional instrumentation by cement mixers, vibrators, cranes, and portable generators. All were unmuffled or inadequately muffled, through economy or through indifference and ignorance. And there was no practical escape from the din.

What happened to the residents of my neighborhood, as I was to learn, is already happening or will soon happen to millions of human and animal receivers of noise. The clatter of a jet or helicopter flight path; the incessant hum of a thruway; "temporary" construction sounds; the multi-level buzz of a dozen modern kitchen conveniences; conversations of neighbors in the next apartment; automated office equipment; the roar of an air conditioner; power lawn mowers, chain saws, and mechanized farm implements—you don't have to live near a subway project to suffer from noise. And nobody, especially in the United States, has any incentive to design for noise control.

It was no secret that upper Sixth Avenue was noisy. Three months after the start of the subway project, an acoustical engineer told a reporter that Manhattan was "the noisiest place in the country and probably the whole world," and upper Sixth Avenue was the worst area in the city.

From 7:00 A.M. to 4:30 P.M., for a period of three years, my family and my neighbors dwelt in a noise environment far higher than that permitted at the property line of factories by New York's zoning code.

One's first reaction to a noise assault of this caliber is to believe, then just hope, then pray that the nagging noise will go away. But it continued. Daytime telephone conversation was possible only during the golden half-hour when the construction workers stopped for lunch. Office personnel were tormented by headaches and other noise-induced ailments, including short tempers. Many of us residents seemed to become absent-minded: neighbors reported taking showers without removing eyeglasses or articles of clothing. We couldn't converse in our own apartments without shouting. The vibrations made windows rattle, and floor vibrations were so pronounced that people wore shoes with ripple soles to counteract them.

Tranquilizers and aspirins were eaten like popcorn. I didn't mind taking sedatives, but I did hate to share them with my two-year-old, as prescribed by our pediatrician. My daughter was starting to talk at that time, and it seems to me her first comprehensible phrase was: "Noisy street, Daddy, stop the noisy street."

Home became a place to be avoided between the hours of 7:00 A.M. and 4:30 P.M. But many who lived in this area worked at home. We dreaded Monday mornings. Comfort became a remembrance of things past, replaced by sleeplessness, ringing in the ears, and headaches.

Doctors could only offer their patients tranquilizers and sympathy. Those with offices in the vicinity were themselves complaining, not only of the discomfort, but of the impossibility of using stethoscopes for diagnosis. A neighborhood drugstore made news because of its phenomenal sale of earplugs; another shop featured acoustic earmuffs in its windows. Down our block, where he was then recuperating from a heart attack (from which he was soon to die), Traffic Commissioner Henry Barnes vowed to take up the noise issue.

Billy Rose eventually stopped coming to his own Ziegfeld Theater office for the duration of the construction. He died before it ended. His staff, forced to remain behind, barricaded the windows with battens of sound-absorbing material, giving up their daylight. I boarded up several of my windows with the same material, not knowing then that it was no obstacle to sound.

The intense noise proved to be an economic as well as a personal blight. Hotels suffered diminished occupancy, with cancelled reservations and shortened stays. Sixth Avenue restaurants and specialty shops were hurt as office workers detoured to Fifth and Seventh Avenues. The Ziegfeld Theater lost bookings, and banks reported a noticeable decrease in business. Real estate rentals dropped. For-rent signs in midtown New York are normally as rare as dodo birds, especially in so convenient a location as upper Sixth Avenue, but now they blossomed in front of the luxury buildings lining the Avenue. Tenants broke leases and moved. One management reported a $7,000-a-month loss in rentals.

We did not get used to the agony of living with nagging, reverberating noise; indeed, we became super-sensitive to other noises.

Naively, I decided to take action.

First I complained to the neighborhood policeman. Patiently, he pulled out a collection of mimeographed notes. One dealt with noise complaints.

"Look!" he said. "There it is in black and white."

I looked. Construction noise from 7:00 A.M. to 6:00 P.M. was exempt from the anti-noise ordinance.

Well, I would appeal directly to the Transit Authority.

This bureaucratic dictatorship, I was to learn, was responsible to no one. The noise, I was flatly told, was the price of progress.

The price was too high. I decided to try the contractor. His representative told me in so many words (that I can't print) that the noise would remain as it was. The contractor told newspaper reporters that "Concentrating the compressors in one spot is the most humane way to handle the problem."

City Councilman (later Congressman and now New York State Supreme Court judge) Theodore Kupferman talked to the contractor, and was told: "Nothing will be done." The representative of the people was as helpless to control the noise as the people themselves.

I wrote to the Commissioner of Health, asking for a meeting. I received no reply, and went over his head to call one of the four doctors on the Board of Health, only to hear that the noise of construction at Bellevue Hospital was disturbing *his* work! Nevertheless, I demanded some attention. Persistence (and threat of a lawsuit) finally made the Health Department act—they passed the buck to the Police Department.

A police sergeant visited me at home, listened politely, and told me he would hear Slattery's side of the story. When I didn't hear from the Police Department within a reasonable time, I wrote to the Sanitary Inspection Division of the Health Department asking for a report. The reply referred me to the Deputy Police Commissioner in charge of community relations. I called that office and was told that it was merely a liaison with the Health Department. I was referred to the Chief Inspector's Office. I called that office and was referred to Patrol Headquarters, Manhattan South. After persistent inquiry, I was told that this project was classified as temporary and "emergency work" and that permits had been issued for necessary drilling, and so forth. (In other words, I had no grounds for complaint.)

And meanwhile the buck continued to be passed. The Transit Authority claimed it was following traditional construction industry practice in accepting the contractor's noise levels. The contractor said he was using the standard equipment available to him. The manufacturer of the air compressors said he was not responsible for the noisy engine that powered his compressors: he had to buy the components that were on the market. GM's Detroit Diesel, manufacturers of engines for compressors, told me it designed engines to meet the needs of the market, and no one was asking for quieter engines.

In April 1965 New York City Transit Authority engineers wrote to Councilman Kupferman that they, and the contractor, were "mindful of the sensitivity of people in this area and are doing whatever we can to reduce all noise to a minimum. Please be assured that we will maintain a continuing watch at this construction site to the end that all reasonable measures are taken to abate any public inconvenience which may arise." Such a good watch was kept that a 65-year-old woman fell to her death through an opening in the planking over the construction.

When Governor Rockefeller refused to intercede with the TA, I tried the Federal level. I asked the Division of Occupational Health of the United States Public Health Service if an official noise survey could be made. I was told: "At the present time the U.S. Public Health Service does not have funds available nor would it be possible for us to do this work unless it was requested by the City of New York." I asked also if the PHS had any recommended standards for community noise, and was told it had none.

I turned then to the private acoustic consultants, who either painted a picture of certain defeat in court or expressed disinterest in working for the noise victim. Their collective advice is embodied in the letter of one sympathetic expert:

1. Silence your apartment.
2. Induce contractor or Transit Authority to muffle.
3. Move out.

It finally struck me that if anything were to be done about noise, the noise receiver himself would have to do it. There was no "George" protecting the public from excessive noise—not on any level of government.

In Europe, I learned, citizens had organized to fight noise so effectively that the struggle had already gone beyond national boundaries. The national organizations were cooperating as the International Association Against Noise (known by its French initials, AICB). This heartening news led to my joining the British Noise Abatement Society. John Connell, its founder and chairman, taught me the first principle of noise abatement: fight with knowledge and strength. With his encouragement, I decided to form a neighborhood noise abatement organization as a first step toward a sane acoustic environment.

I sent out a call for a neighborhood meeting, and on a hot, muggy night in May 1965, a hundred people showed up. I had invited city councilmen and district leaders of both major parties, as well as the Borough President of Manhattan. Councilman Kupferman attended, and the Borough President sent a representative.

A steering committee was appointed, consisting of two lawyers, a civil engineer, an engineering magazine editor, and myself as chairman. We christened the organization the Upper Sixth Avenue Noise Abatement Association (USANAA). There would be no dues, and we would operate as an informal association of neighbors.

After a thorough exploration, the idea of a lawsuit was discarded as being too costly and unlikely to bring any relief. Instead, I was authorized to continue my attempts to draw attention to the problem and to learn all I could about noise abatement.

It is easier to gain an audience with the Pope than it is to meet with a transportation agency commissar. Determined to present to the Transit Authority a bundle of petitions USANAA had gathered, I sought a meeting with one of the TA's three commissioners.

And so it happened that one morning, July 16, 1965, more

than a year after the subway project uprooted our lives, attorney
Ralph Brazen, plus a representative of one of the blighted apartment buildings, and myself found ourselves in the TA's inner
sanctum, face to face with Commissioner Dan Scannell, Chief
Engineer Nathan Brodkin, several lesser engineers, and the contractor's foreman. From the very beginning we were put on the
defensive. There was not one iota of acknowledgment that we
had a legitimate grievance and that something should be done
to lessen the noise. The TA tried to make it seem that I was the
troublemaker, the only one who was stirring up a fuss. The two
responsible citizens with me, and the petitions containing 400
signatures, were conveniently ignored.

The TA officials proved to be ignorant of industrial safety
codes, ignorant of the basic principles of noise measurement and
control, and totally indifferent to our discomfort.

For every point we raised, the Transit Authority had a rebut-
tal.

When the real estate representative reported extensive losses
from leases cancelled and unrenewed because of the excessive
noise, the Chief Engineer tiredly answered, "These tenants are
not disturbed by the noise. They don't like the horrible appearance of the torn-up street. Anyway, if they don't like it, let them
move." This, to a real estate man whose complaint was that the
tenants *were* moving!

Commissioner Scannell had little to say, except that he believed the noise problem was caused by traffic.

When we placed in evidence brochures and other indications
of advances in construction-noise silencing in England, to name
just one country, the Chief Engineer answered that England was
a socialist country, and that the English and the Europeans in
general built more slowly than we did. When I persisted with
data on silenced equipment and techniques available in the
United States, he sucked in his breath and delivered what he
must have thought was the *coup de grâce:* "Do you, Mr. Baron,
by demanding quieter subway construction, wish to jeopardize

the fifteen-cent fare?" Then, turning to his staff, he sighed, "Ah, I can hardly wait until August first when I start my vacation and can get away from this noisy city."

So sure was the Transit Authority of its invincibility, it could lie with ease. When a local radio station, WMCA, came to our assistance and editorialized that "progress doesn't have to be made at the expense of a community's eardrums," the TA asked for and received equal time to rebut. "Every effort," its spokes-man told the radio audience, "has been made to minimize the noise."

The noisemakers also played deaf. The March 1965 issue of *The Bulletin*, published by The General Contractors Associa-tion, contained a paean to the "advances" made in silencing construction equipment. "Why," raved its anonymous author, "it's getting so that the construction industry will have elimi-nated practically all noise with the exception of the raucous yells of the journeymen . . . . In review it is remarkable how little noise is left by the construction industry in its daily activity. The sound of a tuba is a disturber of the peace compared to what the manufacturers have been able to do with the air compressors these days . . . . They purr a muted throbbing hum that is as docile and as soothing as Brahms' *Lullaby.*"

This appeared more than two years before quieter American compressors reached the market.

The TA knew of the misery and ill-will it was causing the residents of upper Sixth Avenue. How else explain its unprece-dented modesty in not decorating the subway project with the names of the Commissioners and the Chief Engineer and the rest of the credits that usually accompany a new project? Even a new subway *entrance* gets a big billboard with everybody's name. But not this immense rare project. Modesty, shame—or a wish to escape additional complaints? Agencies like the Transit Author-ity should be taking the initiative in encouraging the design of quieter equipment. Instead, when USANAA suggested that the rock drills could be accessory-muffled, the TA replied:

There are no rock drills with noise suppressors available. Inquiries to manufacturers of rock drills reveal that there is not enough of a demand for this type of equipment to justify their production. When such equipment is made generally available, its use by subway contractors will be encouraged by the Transit Authority.

Where is this demand to come from, if not from giant public users of such equipment like this very agency?

So USANAA lost the battle of residential Sixth Avenue. But it started a nation-wide renaissance of education and action for noise abatement.

We had learned a good deal. For one thing, it became obvious that the noise problem was no simple neighborhood nuisance, and that what was urgently needed was a community-wide citizens' noise abatement organization with a broad spectrum of members, including physicians, scientists, clergymen, businessmen, noise control experts, and the communications media.

In May 1966 I attended (and addressed) the IVth International Congress for Noise Abatement in Baden-Baden, West Germany. While there I discovered there were noise-reduced air compressors and jackhammers on the market—in Europe; that there were superior noise laws—in Europe; and that Europeans considered noise as more than a mere nuisance. With this information I was able to persuade attorney and writer on public affairs John Wharton to act as one of the founders of what we later named Citizens for a Quieter City, Inc. (CQC). Dr. Samuel Rosen, the eminent ear surgeon and auditory researcher, agreed to serve as Chairman of the Board, and Jerome Nathanson, a Leader, N.Y. Society for Ethical Culture, agreed to serve as President.

During this formative period I kept abreast of noise abatement developments by joining the Acoustical Society of America, reading its *Journal* and attending its meetings and seminars on noise control. In addition I read everything I could find on the subject of noise, its effects on man, and its control.

CQC began operating in January 1967, gradually developing into a recognized "voice of the knowledgeable concerned citizen." We prepared and disseminated a variety of noise abatement literature, experimented with a newsletter, presented papers before professional societies, sent representatives to noise-related meetings, and accepted invitations to testify before government hearings. We encouraged Mayor Lindsay to authorize a Mayor's Task Force on Noise Control. We endorsed the birth of New York City's pioneering Bureau of Noise Abatement. We were responsible for an improvement in the noise insulation provisions of the City's new building code (adopted in November 1968).

More than just raising and clarifying the noise issue, CQC proposed and stimulated solutions.

We initiated New York City's "quiet garbage truck" project, inspired by what I saw in Baden-Baden.

We inspired the development of a quiet metal garbage can, an innovation that became a national symbol of applied noise control.

We also imported, and publicly demonstrated, a quieter jackhammer and air compressor, and reminded the American pneumatic tool industry that the American public was waiting. American versions appeared on the market several months after this demonstration.

Hard work and perseverance was forcing society to move off dead center.

The very existence of CQC became a constant reminder of public concern for noise in the environment. We were cited in government reports, and I was appointed to the Commerce Technical Advisory Board Noise Abatement Panel, U.S. Department of Commerce, established at the direction of the White House in 1968.

The end of the '60s saw the beginning, not of noise abatement, but at least of the setting of ceilings on noise. In 1968 Congress authorized the FAA to certificate aircraft for noise, and in May of 1969 a new regulation required that industry doing more than $10,000 worth of business with the Federal government reduce noise levels so as to not deafen more than ten per cent of its workers.

These noise-oriented activities are only a beginning. Not more than skirmishes against the tyranny of noise.

It may be true that the meek shall inherit the earth, but that will be because it won't be livable, and the noisemaker will be living on other planets. Whether under geodesic domes or under water, the goal for our cities must be as quiet an environment as necessary for human comfort and well-being. This goal is achievable if we end our passive acceptance of industry's acoustic waste products.

PART I

Introduction To Noise

CHAPTER ONE

Today And Tomorrow

George Bernard Shaw entered a posh London restaurant, took a seat, and was confronted by the waiter. "While you are eating, sir, the orchestra will play anything you like. What would you like them to play?"

Shaw's reply? "Dominoes."

We are living in an incredibly noisy world. When I looked I found din in Madrid, where subway construction was chopping up lovely Castellan Avenue. The burghers of Frankfurt or Munich would not have been able to take their fingers out of their ears to sign my petitions; they, too, were experiencing subway construction. And no wonder Governor Rockefeller and the State of New York heard nothing unusual on Sixth Avenue: Albany was being torn down and rebuilt and its reverberating legislative halls were alive with tension and fright (but no anti-noise legislation).

B.D. Allen, chief public health inspector for Coventry, England, has warned that British cities could become "noise hells" in the immediate future. In 1966 Dr. M. G. Candau, Director-General of the World Health Organization, called urban noise a growing world-wide threat.

The theme of the July 1967 *UNESCO Courier* was noise pollution, and its articles were printed in English, French, Spanish, Russian, German, Arabic, Japanese, and Italian.

There is no escape. It doesn't matter whether the head is under a Mexican sombrero or a Wall Street homburg, the wearer is holding his hands to his ears. Moscow's *Vechernaya Moskva* reports that people living near the truck depot on Khodinsky Street cannot sleep because of truck horns and a loudspeaker blaring orders. It further complains of inconsiderate citizens who play loud tape recorders all night long, start car engines at night, or drive around courtyards on noisy motorcycles.

A resident of Pretoria, South Africa, blames church clock chimes for two years of sleeplessness. And in the heart of primitive Africa, missionaries send for ear stopples to keep out the native drumming and noisy ritual dances.

When I was in London for the fifth annual meeting of the International Congress for Noise Abatement, I had to give up a cheerful bay window room because it fronted on Knightbridge Road, throbbing with buses, cars, and lorries. Later I stopped off to enjoy the peace and quiet—so I imagined—of Ireland. Dublin was no haven; I had to change rooms three times in a first-class hotel, once to escape the traffic, a second time to escape the clatter and chatter from the kitchen, and a third time to escape the roaring central exhaust fan installed in the courtyard.

That fewer and fewer people are able to escape excessive noise was further revealed in a report of the Greater London Council published in 1965. It revealed that a large proportion of the population of London, indoors, with windows slightly open, is subject to noise levels in excess of those suggested as acceptable maxima by a government-sponsored committee in 1960.

We further learn that in London there is only a brief period of quiet during the 24 hours of each day. The Greater London Council reports that though the average levels at night are much lower than by day, "the quietest period only lasts from 1:00 A.M. to 5:00 A.M. Between 10:00 P.M. and midnight, when many people go to bed, and during the hour or so before they normally wake up, noise levels are comparatively high, and at these times disturbance is likely to be less tolerated."

So pressing is the noise problem becoming, the Greater London Council has established one laboratory in its scientific laboratories solely devoted to sound and vibration, and European cities such as Zurich have assigned noise control functions to both their police and health departments.

These are but a few illustrations that the problem is worldwide and today's noises are of much greater significance than yesterday's. The noise victim is not alone in his suffering. And he has every reason for feeling disturbed. He is surrounded by an excess of noisemakers, motor-driven machines and devices that are not designed for quiet operation.

Though the largest cities, such as New York, Tokyo, Rio de Janeiro, and Madrid vie with each other for the title of "noisiest," noise is no longer exclusively a large-city problem. Neither is it solely a problem of industrialized societies. From Addis Ababa to the western provinces of Zambia, the unmuffled operations and products of industry assail the ears. Natives of Nairobi join with New Yorkers and Muscovites in complaining about the noises of traffic and the din of horns. And Moto Nkama, young diplomat from Zambia assigned to the United Nations, does not find New York's noises strange. His mother's house was next to a copper smelter, and he grew up to the sounds of rocks falling off conveyor belts, "the bars of copper dropping with a crash."

Appearing as a guest on the Johnny Carson *Tonight* Show, I asked TV viewers to send me their particular noise. I knew the noise sources, but I wanted their geographical distribution. Sure enough, some 1,400 noise complaints poured in from every state of the Union, including Alaska and Hawaii. Farmers, small-town folks, owners of vacation homes and city residents alike asked where they could buy the acoustic earmuffs demonstrated on that show. It is a shock to note the growth of noise complaints in the smaller towns and villages. The escape hatch from the stresses of the large city has traditionally been to flee to the "country," and now that escape hatch is closing down.

The network of highways brings noise intrusion into the suburb. Medina, Washington, on the outskirts of Seattle, is trying to fend off freeway noise with a decibel limit enforced by its one policeman with a sound-level meter. The Sierra Club has reported that in the Humboldt Redwood State Park in California, "not a single grove in the park is beyond the sound of passing traffic." One harassed New Yorker was sadly disillusioned upon trying to escape to the pastoral quiet of New Hampshire: "I have moved from my apartment for three months to escape the jackhammers, garbage trucks and airplanes . . . only to find that the local sawmill has installed a new machine that is louder than all three New York instruments put together." Another New Yorker who bought a home in New Hampshire for summer use discovered that whereas in New York he was forced to wake up at 7:00 A.M. by legalized construction and other mechanized noises, in the wilds of New Hampshire he was awakened at 5:00 A.M. by chain-saw-wielding tree cutters who started out before dawn to avoid the heat of the day.

Noise pollution was at first endemic in the large cities, and in recent years their newspapers have been up in arms with anti-noise editorials. But a chilling omen of things to come is the appearance of such editorials in small-town newspapers like the Martha's Vineyard *Gazette* (inveighing against loud motorcycles and airport expansion) and this one from the Milford *Cabinet*, published in Milford, New Hampshire, population 3,916:

July 4, 1968.—NOW "NOISE POLLUTION." . . . Noise pollution is what we suffer from when we sit on the rocks looking out to sea enjoying the sense of the wind and the waves, but not enjoying at all the blast of soul music from the transistor radio on a nearby table.

Noise pollution is what shatters the neighborhood calm when one of those undersized motorcycles without a muffler goes up the road in the evening. Noise pollution is the convertible with the top down and the radio turned up high, which parks in front of the house before taking off with a screech of tires on asphalt. . . .

Noise pollution emanates from the whole gamut of bulldozers, tractors, loaders, scrapers and trucks that we accept as the tools of our civilization. Noise pollution is the high-powered outboard motor, which scatters a flock of ducklings and destroys any illusions of peace that might have been sought by people along the shore of any of a thousand New England lakes. . . .

Even running away to our presumably quieter neighbor to the north has its hazards. Canada's *Maclean's* Magazine warns city dwellers planning to buy a quiet farm to forget it. Farmers, the magazine reported, are becoming as deaf as fence posts because of "overexposure to noise."

The Dean of the University of Illinois School of Agriculture lists the problems to be caused by building industrial complexes on farm land as one of the challenges that must be faced by agricultural specialists.

So where does one go for quiet? Honolulu, where the pressure of complaints led to formation of a Mayor's Committee on Noise Control? The Virgin Islands, with a new jetport for St. Thomas and St. Croix? Snowmobile country in the north woods?

To students of industrialization and technological development, the extent of today's noise will come as no surprise. Nor will it be a surprise to the students of the population explosion. The rural population is flocking to the cities (to get away from those noisy tractors). Congestion alone is bringing noises closer to the receiver.

I now live in a giant housing complex of 4,000 apartments. My neighbors may be among the 40,000 working in the 15 acres of Rockefeller Center. Some share office space with 25,000 others in the Pan Am Building.

The insatiable pressure for housing is forcing human beings to live in intensely noisy housing sites. For example, a federation of trade unions, civic groups, and housing cooperatives is sponsoring Twin Pines Village, a New York State-financed cooperative to be built three miles from the end of two frequently used runways at Kennedy International Airport. Its sponsors are proceeding with this project in spite of the warnings of the Federal Aviation Administrator that "individual reactions resulting from noise exposure of this intensity would likely include vigorous complaints." The sponsors reply that they will insulate the roof, use double window panes, and install central air conditioning so the windows will not have to be opened in warm weather. And for the outdoors—fingers in the ears?

The pressure for housing, and the shortage and expense of city land, are forcing planners, unwisely, to build housing over "air rights." A complex of four 32-story buildings, with a mortgage financed by the state, was constructed on platforms over the Bronx approach to the George Washington Bridge. When it was opened in 1964, unsuspecting tenants moved in, only to find themselves subjected to the exhaust fumes and noise of the heavily traveled twelve-lane highway under the apartments. No one had ever thought of motor vehicles as sources of noise and pollution.

Noise is nothing new. Even the main reasons for most noise —convenience and speed—are as old as the first squeaky wheel. Chariots racing noisily over Rome's cobblestones forced Julius Caesar to try—unsuccessfully—to ban daytime charioteering. The unwanted sounds of the past were less intense, less frequent, traveled shorter distances, and reached fewer ears.

Some would like us to think we have merely traded new noises for old. But the acoustic attack on man and his environment really began in earnest with the Industrial Revolution. From a predominantly agricultural husbandry, man found himself uprooted by the pull of the factories to the grime and congestion of the cities. He found himself surrounded on all sides by factories making millions of devices to enable him to speed over the surface of the earth, soar through the skies, and blend orange juice.

Men by the millions work in these factories. They operate noisy machines to noisily blast, buff, chip, stamp, punch, forge, grind, and polish metal; saw, plane, sandblast and polish wood; press ink on paper; weave wire and textiles, and work all kinds of plastics. Fabricated parts—bearings, pistons, gears, levers, fan blades—are assembled into devices that turn, rotate, blow, slide and push, and explode. The noisy components are welded, mechanically screwed, bolted and glued into visually attractive outer shells and pushed openly on the markets of the world.

Behind their high-style façades, air conditioners, for example, generate the complex sounds of: magnetic hum, reciprocating compressor put-put, fan-generated pure tones, and cycling noise, described as a combination of clatter from piston slap and magnetic hum. Fans in ventilating systems and air conditioners, or just plain electric fans, generate noise because of imbalance, bearings, brushes, gears and magnetic hum. Communities in which many homes use heat pumps and window units are described as sounding like beehives. A curious acoustical engineer took noise level readings one evening in a narrow New York street, surrounded by high-rise luxury buildings, each with its own air conditioner unit. There were no lullabies in the 90-plus decibel levels. The new type of unit used for detached homes leaves the condensing unit outdoors for the neighbors to hear. These units are so noisy, manufacturers advertise that new designs direct most of the noise upward instead of at the neighbors.

Mechanical marvels transport man and his goods by land, by sea, and by air with explosive-type engines that propel his vehicles; certain types of planes now traverse the air so rapidly, sound cannot keep up. Powerful mechanized versions of the pickaxe and the sledgehammer build the places he is going to, and the roads to get there—air compressors, jackhammers, piledrivers, steam shovels, bulldozers, compactors, rock drills.

Many of the more delicate mechanisms are called appliances and they provide man with convenience and comfort once his shelter is built. They are available in infinite variety to use in the kitchen to refrigerate his perishables, freeze his ice cream, make ice cubes, crush ice, grind his meat, juice his fruit, electrically cut, slice and shred, mix and blend his food, open cans, purify water, broil, masticate the garbage, exhaust the smells of it all, and wash the dishes.

Other appliances speed him through his bathroom operations with dispatch and a minimum of effort. All he has to do is stand at a stooped attention and give the toothbrush salute, and electric motors will squirt water into every dental nook and cranny, polish every ivory. With no more effort than moving his arm up and down, his stubble is removed from under a lather which just slithered into his hand from the mechanical lather-making machine. If he has time to sit in a tub, a hydrotherapy machine will spare him the need to paddle the water around.

No sultan in his harem had the mechanical servants modern man has in his living room. Consider the devices to cool air, purify air, warm air, push air, while mechanical fingers massage his aching frame as he reclines in his motorized vibrating lounge chair.

When he has used his electric shoe polisher and is ready to retire for the night, he has a massage machine and an electrically operated bed. His wife has a mechanical hair dryer (4.3 million were sold in 1967), an electric manicure outfit, and even an electric razor.

And for all rooms, TV sets, radios, stereos, tape machines, and for creative self-expression, amplified instruments. Not to mention mechanical hobby tools—including chain saws—and lawn mowers. It is almost impossible to find a home that does not have at least one radio and one television set. In the last twenty years the electronics industry has sold more than 450 million radios, 130 million television sets, 83 million phonographs, 33 million tape recorders and playback units. The industry estimates that more than 515 million consumer electronic instruments are in use today, and these products are selling at a rate of 75 million annually.

One of the latest noise sources is the siren-like burglar alarm. Installed in automobiles and in homes, their owners are usually not around when they go off. Innocent neighbors, in increasing numbers, are being forced to endure hours of agonizing mechanical screams.

Without regulation, toys have joined the decibel madness, and are designed with noise as a sales feature. Velocipedes are equipped with simulated motor noises, plus horns. Toy carbide cannons make a mighty roar that can be heard for blocks. The acoustician reviewing a patent for a device designed to sound like a one-cylinder motorcycle engine was provoked to comment: "The joy of making noise is the birthright of every youngster, but must he have a battery-powered machine to make it for him?"

Animal noise, too, is proliferating. Possibly to assuage the increasing coldness and alienation of urban living, apartment dwellers are taking to pets. It is estimated that whereas five to ten per cent kept pets five years ago, the odds are that one out of six now has a dog or cat.

One of the major reasons for today's noisy world is the mobile noise source of vehicles. Trucks and buses are especially obnoxious. London studies have shown that if the traffic mix reaches 50 per cent heavy vehicles, there is a doubling of loudness over traffic with only 20 per cent heavy vehicles. According to that survey, when traffic moves on even a slight gradient, there is an increase in noise, and under these circumstances, trucks are the the worst offenders. A truck can almost double its noise level on a 1-in-20 gradient at 30 mph.

Unpleasant noise exposure is a combination of power and the number of times that a powerful source makes itself heard. The aviation industry is providing us with both exposure to incredibly powerful—and noisy—motors, and millions of exposures.

The Federal Aviation Administration handled 41 million landings and takeoffs in 1966, recording 1,925 landings and takeoffs in one day that year at Chicago's O'Hare International

Airport. An average of one a minute. New York Congressman Joseph P. Addabbo has reported as many as one movement every 30 seconds at Kennedy International Airport. When a typical long-range, four-engine jet transport lands, approximately eight square miles of land outside the airport are exposed to generally unacceptable noise levels. This is a conservative estimate of the area rendered intolerable.

No wonder the Federal Council for Science and Technology could report that "the over-all loudness of environmental noise is doubling every ten years."

Let us imagine that John Doe and his family want to escape some of these noise sources, not by running away to some South Sea island, but by being able to close the door of their home. This form of escape, too, is disappearing. Whether he pays $100 a month in a low-income housing project, or can afford $1,000 for a postwar luxury apartment, it is fairly certain he will hear the steps, jumps, radio, TV, dropped toys, and furniture-moving of the people in the apartment above. Paradoxically, as his world grew noisier, John Doe's dwelling space was built to allow that noise to enter. Gone are the dwellings of fifty years ago with their heavy walls and rooms separated from each other by tight-fitting doors. Returning after World War II, Private John Doe was rewarded by the building industry with some of the noisiest buildings in existence.

Even those new glass office buildings with their glittering façades can be a nightmare to work in. Dr. Athelstan Spilhaus, President of the Franklin Institute, Philadelphia, describes his reaction to this type of postwar construction: "I recently saw a building on Park Avenue, one of those glass boxes. They were tearing up the street outside, of course. The architect asked me if it weren't beautiful from the outside. I couldn't hear him, fortunately. Inside, in order to preserve the open space and the beautiful visual environment, he had kept the walls down low. The office racket added to the racket of the street, beautifully transmitted through the glass. So it was the environment of a boiler factory. I told him later, when we managed to get where we could talk, that only the stone deaf could have enjoyed the visual experience."

This unprecedented noise exposure, plus the increasing scarcity of areas of escape, is distressing millions of human beings. And not only the popular stereotype of "the little old lady in tennis shoes" (meaning by that someone who has nothing better to do than complain about something), but heads of state, government officials, and responsible citizens, are upset. A distinguished architectural acoustician and former Chancellor of the University of California, Dr. Vern Knudsen, finds noise "the scourge of the twentieth century." Dr. Rosen of CQC describes noise as a "molester." Other noise victims describe noise as something that drives them wild, gives them a headache, makes them nauseous and dizzy, keeps them from sleeping. Even the cow is affected by noise, and to a farmer, noise means less milk yield. Society now speaks of "noise pollution," "ear pollution," "audio pollution," and "audible harassment." It is so noisy that the *Handbook of Noise Measurement* lists 106 words "commonly used to describe sounds of various types." These range from bang and bark through ping, pop, pow, to rattle, scrunch, squeak, and thud, thump, and yap.

Noise is even penetrating the subconscious. A disc jockey started to read a weather report just handed to him: ". . . very loudy today." He stopped, and broke up laughing. He then predicted that in the future there will be noise reports—mildly loudy, impossibly loudy, and so on.

Noise is such an omnipresent part of our lives that to many it is the "natural" accompaniment of civilization, the "price of progress," with the jackhammer as its symbol. To mark the opening of that Sixth Avenue subway extension, businessmen placed full-page newspaper ads featuring a happy jackhammer operator. It was a shock to me to see him again in a public service ad promoting religion in American life. Presumably the advertising agency saw him as a happy symbol of progress.

Some city people believe that it would detract from the function of the subway if the trains were pleasingly quiet and stations were designed for tranquility. A young but able and imaginative New York architect told me he would not want to design a subway train so quiet that its riders and those waiting in the station would be unaware there was a train in their midst. Neither did he want the subway stations to look "like the lobby of the Plaza Hotel." He cautioned me against trying to make the city too quiet. He wanted New York to maintain a certain level of sound energy as a desirable aspect of city life. Perhaps he was also being considerate of the needs of the wife of a Midwest manufacturer of musical instruments who enjoys noise and "imports" tapes of New York street noises to sleep by!

Partly because of the duality within each of us as both makers and receivers of noise, we wish to be free to make noise ourselves, even if we may not enjoy the noise made by others. "The North American motoring public," reports George Thiessen, a Canadian government researcher, "has a split personality about the growing problems of traffic noise. As homeowners they would like to enjoy an evening out of doors in peace and quiet, but as motorists they want the maximum power to give maximum acceleration even if the tires squeal. They like to hear their vroom, or at least some of them do."

It is a commonplace that noisemaking is associated with virility, and that objections to noise are associated with a lack of masculinity. To protect oneself from noise, let alone complain, is also deemed unmanly. In a lecture on noise, one acoustical expert related a personal experience during his early years working in a factory. He literally had watched a colleague go deaf. "It took five to six years. He was working in a test block at Republic Aviation. He was too much of a man, he thought, to wear earmuffs."

Motorcycle (and sports car) manufacturers design to satisfy the demand for conspicuous noisemaking. The theories behind this demand are many, ranging from the use of noise as a protective device to ward off the drivers of bigger cars and trucks to the concept of noise as a mating call. Why would any sexually frustrated motorcyclist support noise-control legislation if he equates noisy motorcycling with lovemaking? The sex-via-noise theory was reported to the American Psychiatric Association by Harvard psychiatrist Dr. Armand N. Nicholi, Jr. According to one press report, Dr. Nicholi believes that some sexually troubled college-age men relieve their feelings of sexual inadequacy with "an unusual preoccupation with the motorcycle." Though he described his patients as expressing fears of death and castration when they discussed motorcycle riding, he also reported on the "appeal of . . . the intrusion of the deafening noise into other people's ears . . ." as suggesting a genital or phallic feature. This line of thinking suggests that the big-city cab driver is not blowing his horn to satisfy his passenger's desire for speed. It also suggests that "showboating," as columnist Russell Baker describes the unnecessary use of fire engine sirens, may not mean that the firemen are saying to the taxpayers, "See how productive I am." With very little stretching, Dr. Nicholi's sexual aberration theory might give the public grounds for attacking noisy motorcyclists and motorists as perpetrators of aural sodomy.

New York's 1930 Noise Commission psyched the horn-honking driver. "Even in free flowing traffic, some motorists appear to take an almost fiendish delight in sounding their horns when there is nothing in the way." Today's American motorists object to the quieter city horn on European imports, and some European car manufacturers are discontinuing the export of the dual city-country horn to the United States.

I once naively told a horn-blowing New York cab driver, "You're violating the law."

"What law?" he smirked. "My elbow slipped."

In contrast, a Cockney cab driver taught me a lesson in driver attitude. We were caught in rush-hour traffic on the way to Heathrow Airport. Several times other vehicles cut in front of us.

Each time, conditioned by those New York cabbies, I braced for the retaliatory horn. Silence. Finally, after a third such incident, my horn-conditioned nervous system couldn't take the suspense, and I asked the driver, "Why didn't you blow your horn? Is it against the law?"

"No, it's not against the law. Only at night. I didn't toot because it's not good manners. Besides, might rattle the chap."

Is the horn honker a sadist? The horn-blowing truck driver or motorcyclist who has gutted his muffler may not be as interested in expressing his virility as he is in acting out a need for inflicting pain. If the operator and the manufacturer of noisy machines are unconsciously working out sadistic tendencies that exist in many of us, the rationale behind objections to noise-control legislation becomes clear.

This innate desire to make noise and to inflict noise on others may be one explanation of the electronic noise explosion. That the rapid growth of television and stereo is likely more than a hunger for culture is indicated in a paper by Dr. H. Angus Bowes presented before the Psychiatric Research Association in 1957. As reported in *Time* Magazine, his "Psychopathology of the Hi-Fi Addict" contained this revealing passage: "Naturally, the less organized will treat their hi-fi set rather like the emotionally immature treat a car—as an expression of aggression, as a power symbol. To many [hi-fi] has a sexual connotation. Perhaps in the twiddling of knobs, there may be a masturbatory equivalent. Certainly the ability to take control of a situation relieves anxiety and what control is given to the manipulator of a hi-fi apparatus when, with a flick of the wrist, he may attenuate his treble, emphasize his bass, turn down the volume to a whisper, or blast the neighbors with a Niagara of sound."

Manufacturers of audio equipment are not unaware of the needs they are satisfying. A Fisher Radio advertisement offered "Power! Power! The power to unleash wattage and make an almighty noise is a favorite fantasy of the hi-fi extremist. . . . Take, for example, the devastatingly powerful Fisher system.

. . . The 700-T and the two XP-18s can blast the roof off your house if you have an itchy volume-control finger."

This kind of intense noisemaking is not all give. The maker wants to hear, as well. Some of us want to be "turned on" with sound. This phenomenon parallels the increasing use of LSD, marijuana, and other means of getting high. A member of one of the popular electronically-amplified combos, the Grateful Dead, told a reporter from *The New York Times*: "Part of our thing is to try to turn people on with our music, because if you're up tight you can't relax." This new music-to-relax-by can sound like a "derailed freight train plunging over a cliff." Audiences enjoy this new listening experience. When the Butterfield Blues Band blasted away in New York's Town Hall behind ten massed amplifiers, the bulk of the audience did not find it too loud. Audiences are also responding favorably to the use of multimedia, an attack on all senses with intense light, sound, colors, smells, visual images, combinations of high decibel rock'n'roll, wailing sirens, simulated thunderclaps—all used to blitz the audience.

Scientists who work in the field of noise are fatalists. They equate noise with progress, and the future with noise. They believe advancing civilizations will create more noise, not less.

The key to tomorrow's noise is quantum, a dramatic jump in noise sources, noise intensities, and human sensitivity. At the same time, there will be a decrease in our ability to escape.

Demographers predict that by the year 2000, 50 per cent of the population of the United States will live in three supercities: "Boswash," a megalopolis stretching from Boston to Washington, D.C.; "Chipitt," stretching from Chicago to Pittsburgh; and "Sansan," encompassing the area from San Diego to San Francisco.

There may be as many urban buildings constructed in the next 40 to 50 years as in all mankind's history.

Cities and suburbs alike will reverberate to the roar of the jackhammer and the air compressor as they strain to accommodate the 80 per cent of the population expected to live in urban areas by 1985. Some idea of what it will be like is already heard in New York City, with its annual average of 10,000 demolitions plus 80,000 street repair projects. To add acoustic insult to the "normal" construction noise injury, the construction industry is planning to use helicopters to place heavy slabs of concrete and other building parts into position. The Westchester County, New York, local of the International Union of Operating Engineers (its members operate air compressors) is training some of its members to operate helicopters for that purpose.

Bedlam, anyone?

But this will only be the frosting on the acoustic cake. By the year 2000, 73 per cent of the estimated 180 million cars in the United States may be distributed among the 235 million people projected as dwellers in metropolitan centers. Each vehicle has the potential of brake screech, horn blowing, engine noise, and tire noise.

Probably aware of the potential road block, civilization is moving ahead with the development of high-speed train service. This is fine if somebody designs a quieter engine. If not, a new dimension in sound will be added to the lives of those living adjacent to the railroad tracks. They will hear the "screaming electric motors" as the trains roar by "in a terrifying swoosh of noise." Or at least that's what is expected by the reporter for *The New York Times* who covered the first public test of a new high-speed train for service between New York and Washington.

As bad as the future looks in terms of noise from surface traffic, the greatest threat to acoustic sanity is posed by the vehicles that will be shuttling back and forth on aerial corridors in the sky. It almost seems as if all dials are "go" for the human race to noisily take to the air.

One hybrid form of transportation is the hovercraft. This vehicle "floats" on a cushion of air a few feet off the surface, which may be either land or water. It has not yet been clearly defined as aerial, marine, or surface transportation. But whatever else it is, there's no doubt that it is noisy.

Private pleasure hovercraft are entering the market, and what noisy skimobiles are to the winter sportsman, noisy hovercraft are becoming for the summer recreation-seeker. There are models powered by 100-hp outboard motors, models powered by 30-hp air-cooled foreign car motors. One model can travel over lake, river, snow, and marsh areas. In England a do-it-yourself kit has been developed and in 1966 Britons were warned by one newspaper reporter to brace themselves for the new din of home-made hovercraft, "a new menace to British eardrums, including those of horses, cows, and sheep in once peaceful, rural retreats."

And out in America's winter wonderlands it's no longer the sound of sleigh bells ringing but snowmobiles roaring.

As if to guarantee that no habitat will be free of the noise of jet engines, the Department of Defense (DOD) is now developing a jet belt that enables its wearer to fly over buildings and streets. Powered by a small fan-jet engine, it promises a new contender for any list of ten most unwanted sounds.

But these developments are nothing compared to what's in store in "normal" aviation. So rapid is aviation development that only statistics do it justice. Projections for the decade ending 1977 are for an increase in passenger miles flown from 76 billion in 1966 to 266 billion in 1977. To serve these passengers the aviation industry will provide more and larger planes and more airports. The FAA forecast is for 180,000 general aviation planes to be produced by 1977, plus 3,500 transports. This increased volume of aircraft is creating a demand for more jetports. The thousands of planes aloft during the day now require 10,000 landing facilities. As of September 1, 1969, 259 were needed for jets. The FAA projects another 132 jetports by 1974. The pressure for jetport expansion is being met by strong resistance by a public unwilling to put up with such a noisy neighbor.

Jet takeoffs and landings are responsible for much of what it is like to live with aviation noise. The FAA projection to 1977 is that its air control towers will be handling an increase of landings and takeoffs from 41.2 million to 139 million.

What is in store for the nation's larger cities is indicated by the prediction that Los Angeles International Airport will handle 80 million passengers a year. Skeptics doubt that the Boeing 747 and the projected 900-passenger C-5 Galaxy will significantly reduce the number of plane movements.

Tomorrow means an increase in the number of people subjected to jet noise, and an increase in the number of exposures. Part of that increase in noise exposure is caused by the increasing distance from the airport in which jet noise makes itself felt. Where once complaints stopped at a radius of four miles from the airport, the growing blanket of jet noise now radiates a distance of fifteen miles from airports, and further.

Formerly pastoral resort and spa areas are being encroached upon. Witness the recommendation of the Hudson River Valley Commission, which believes that to increase the over-all values of the Valley there is need for landing fields to accommodate the rise in recreational travel by air. It suggested a study to prepare a plan for a system of small landing strips to provide access to recreation areas, "with proper controls to assure that users of such areas are not disturbed by aircraft noise." Given today's airplane engines, what kind of controls does this Commission have in mind?

If there is one immutable law that governs aviation development, it is escalation. More and larger aircraft, and more and more airports, not only in and around large cities but in the small towns of America.

On March 5, 1969, the Lakeland High School in Shrub Oak, New York, was jammed, but not with students. From 7:30 P.M. until midnight, the State Joint Legislative Committee on Mass Transportation held a public hearing to assess public opinion on the proposed Somers Airport. Except for the Metropolitan Transportation Authority, a state agency promoting more airports, all the spokesmen—town supervisors, high school principals, conservationists, and representatives of citizens' anti-airport groups—were opposed.

The Somers facility, proposed for the heart of a suburban-exurban-rural region, would generate enough noise to preclude Federal Housing Authority mortgages, to interfere with the classroom activities of more than a dozen schools, to require close to half-a-million dollars for soundproofing schools, and to force the rezoning of valuable residential property for commercial and industrial use. Somers was rejected as a site, but the FAA, in cooperation with state, regional, and local authorities, has recommended a nationwide development of new general aviation airports and the expansion of smaller airports.

There is now a more immediate threat to the cities, and its initials are V/STOL, vertical and short takeoff and landing planes. (These include helicopters.)

To relieve congestion at the major airports, the FAA and the aviation industry, in cooperation with local and state governments, are promoting V/STOLs for interurban service. The STOL can take off in a short run of a few hundred feet. The VTOL takes off and lands straight up and down, and then cruises like a fixed-wing aircraft. Because of the relatively small space requirements, these craft are deemed feasible for mid-city areas. There are today some 55 VTOL projects around the world, and in the back of the minds of their developers is the anticipated market for interurban transportation.

Morris Ketchum, a past president of the American Institute of Architects, told New York's First Conference on Urban Noise Control, in March 1967, that he predicted city planners will set aside land for use of STOLcraft on cleared lots, abandoned piers, atop railroad stations, over railroad tracks. A few months after Mr. Ketchum's predictions, the senior vice president of Eastern Airlines reported that air traffic delays were costly, and he recommended STOL planes for short hauls between cities in the Northeast Corridor, stretching from Boston to Washington. In October 1967, the Civil Aeronautics Board (CAB) was already investigating the need for V/STOL service in Boston, Hartford, Providence, New York, Newark, Philadelphia, Wilmington, Trenton, Baltimore, and Washington.

The FAA 1968 *National Airport Plan* recommends 25 STOL-ports for the New York-Washington, D.C. corridor and the West Coast. Nine are scheduled for New York City.

Nassau County and New Jersey communities are evolving plans for STOLcraft operations to Manhattan, with, as one idea, landing pads to be built in the rivers around the island.

What will happen to the urban environment when New York, for example, at only *one* STOLport site, accommodates an expected 14 million passengers a year plus two million tons of cargo? And how will downtown Los Angeles fare, and Anaheim, and the area around the STOLport in your city or suburb or small town?

The acoustical consulting firm of Bolt, Beranek and Newman has stated in its house organ *Activities*, "The development of vertical takeoff-and-landing planes might eliminate some of the nuisance around large airports but it would spread the problem [of noise nuisance] to many other locations."

Proponents try to lessen opposition by claiming the approaches and takeoffs will be either over water or in non-residential areas. But these planes are designed to fly at low altitudes and it is difficult to visualize a flight path that avoids residential areas, schools, hospitals, and parks. As a matter of aviation safety, the height of office buildings makes flight paths over residential areas safer and thus more desirable.

V/STOLs are not butterflies.

Gird for protest.

Tomorrow's noise will be more disturbing and crueler than today's, for two reasons. First, we are increasing the number of noise sources and saturating the entire environment. Second, we are becoming sensitized to noise.

From England comes this observation from a Senior Lecturer

in Acoustics at the University of Liverpool:

"Our reactions at a particular instant depend among other factors on our noise history; we are also becoming more noise conscious. . . . We have a tendency to create more noise and a growing awareness of noise."

We may be becoming less tolerant because, as some authorities believe, noise assault is cumulative and the threshold of sensitivity is lowered with increased exposure.

We have not yet begun to cope with the noisy bus and truck and jet, and already we are extending the welcome mat to new intrusive noise sources. When rivers become aviation runways and the space over center-city is nothing but elevator shafts for helicopters and escalator space for STOLs, city-man is going to feel he is living in the center of the Iron Maiden. Not to mention the sonic boom carpet to be thrown over people not living near the large metropolitan center (to be discussed in detail in Chapter 5).

CHAPTER TWO

The Vocabulary Of Noise

In 1967 the Scali, McCabe, Sloves advertising agency volunteered to prepare public service advertising for Citizens for a Quieter City. President Marvin Sloves, copy chief Ed McCabe, and creative director Sam Scali spent weeks poring over a small library of noise reference material. They ended up confused as to the technical nature of noise, but clear about one point: the noise problem is easier to solve than to understand.

The scientists who work in the field of noise have tended to concentrate on those aspects of noise which are readily demonstrable and measurable. The emphasis is on the physics of sound, the sense of hearing, and the attempt to find formulae for measuring and predicting "annoyance" reactions.

The public—and many of its elected officials and government administrators—is intimidated by an alphabet soup of decibels and noise scales. It is almost as if the noisy machine is protected by a wall of measuring systems and units. Trying to define noise and quantify human response has become a substitute for seeking to achieve a less noise-stressed civilization. Quality is dictated by statistics and formulae, not by intuition and common sense.

Noise is defined by the American National Standards Institute as:

(1) any undesired sound
(2) an erratic, intermittent, or statistically random oscillation

A Federal report on the subject was titled *Noise: Sound Without Value*. It would be more accurate to define noise as destructive sound.

Since almost any sound can at some time be a noise, noise is, first and foremost, sound. The study of sound phenomena has been the domain of the physicist, and we owe a debt of gratitude to the physical sciences—and the audiologists—for uncovering the nature and behavior of the sound wave.

Sound is a three-fold phenomenon: the *source*—a vibrating object or material, something that has been excited; the *transmission* of the vibration; and the *effect*—the sensory perception called hearing, plus a complex of physiological and psychological reactions.

One way of understanding how sound is generated is to visualize a vibrating object. When, for example, a tuning fork is struck, it vibrates back and forth. When it moves in one direction, it compresses the air molecules in its path; when it reverses direction the air in its former path becomes less compressed, or rarefied. Each time the vibrating object moves back and forth there is one complete cycle of pressure change, and this pulsating compression/rarefaction is radiated outward from the source. The effect of this oscillation on the medium on which the vibration takes place—in this case air—is called the sound wave.

Acousticians use the term cycles-per-second (cps) to express the frequency of sound waves—and thus their pitch.

The relative intensity of sound is usually measured in decibels. Although decibels are not easy to understand, some facts, and Table 1, will make it possible to feel a little more comfortable with the term.

So sensitive is the human ear that it can hear a wide range of sound pressures, with a spread of many millions of pressure units. This wide range has been compressed into a more workable range of 0 to 140 decibels (somewhat higher if we include such sounds as cannon fire and rocket noise). Unlike inches or cubic centimeters, decibels are on a dimensionless scale of values.

The decibel system has several unique features. Though its basic reference point is 0 decibels, zero is not silence or the absence of sound. Zero decibels represents the threshold of audible sound for a healthy young set of ears.

More important, decibels do not progress arithmetically; decibels are logarithmic. This means that each change of decibel level represents a sizeable change in acoustic energy, enabling the system to cope with the wide range of audible sound. Another rationale for the use of a logarithmic system is that the ear perceives differences in sound intensity logarithmically. A decibel represents the smallest change in sound intensity detectable by the human ear.

To give an idea of decibel progression, a given sound at 10 decibels has ten times the intensity of a sound at 0 decibels; at 20 decibels it has 100 times the intensity at 0 decibels; and at 30 decibels it has 1,000 times the intensity at 0 decibels, etc. We can say then that decibels are small numbers that represent large quantities of sound energy. Decibels are measured with a sound level meter.

Originally the "C" decibel was in common usage, expressed as dB(C). This measured the sound pressure on a flat scale. Then it was discovered that the human ear was not as sensitive to the lower frequencies as to the higher, and so the "A" decibel, dB(A), was born. When a decibel meter is switched to the "A" scale, some 40 decibels at the lower frequencies are filtered out of the measurement. This means that a noise source having much of its acoustic energy in the lower frequencies will have a lower dB(A) reading than dB(C). By coincidence, some of the most disturbing noise sources, such as transportation, have much of their acoustic energy in the lower frequencies.

The decibel levels of some familiar noise sources and environments are shown in Table 1. Tables such as this indicate the relative intensities of various sounds. We should remember that magnitude, or "how many decibels" is only one dimension of noise.

The transmission of sound waves must take place in a medium —gas, liquid, or solid. According to the American National Standards Institute, "The medium in which the source exists is often indicated by an appropriate adjective: e.g., airborne, waterborne, structureborne." Your neighbor's footsteps overhead are creating structureborne sounds. Your neighbor's lawn mower is creating airborne sounds.

Sound is commonly produced by the vibration of a solid: solids striking other solids, solids rubbing against solids (friction). Musical sounds, for example, may be created by the vibration of a plucked string, the friction of bow against strings, or the vibration of a struck surface, as a drumhead. Airborne sound may be caused by turbulence, the agitation produced when a rapidly moving air stream hits still air, as in jet exhaust; or when a rapidly moving air stream hits an obstruction, as when the stream of air from a fan hits a poorly designed fan guard or grille. Other examples of sound created by turbulence in the air are the notes of wind instruments, created by fluctuations in an air column, and the sounds created when rapidly flowing air strikes the open window of a speeding car.

Compared to other forms of power, such as electricity or a combustion engine, the sound wave's power appears minuscule.

TABLE 1

TYPICAL DECIBEL [dB(A)] VALUES ENCOUNTERED
IN DAILY LIFE AND INDUSTRY

	dB(A)		dB(A)
Rustling Leaves	20	Loudly Reproduced Orchestral Music in Large Room)	82
Room in a Quiet Dwelling at Midnight	32	(Beginning of Hearing Damage, if Prolonged)	85
Soft Whisper at Five Feet	34	Printing Press Plant (Medium Size Automatic)	86
Men's Clothing Dept. of Large Store	53	Heavy City Traffic	92
Window Air Conditioner	55	Heavy Diesel Propelled Vehicle (about 25 ft. away)	92
Conversational Speech	60	Air Grinder	95
Household Dept. of Large Store	62	Cut-off Saw	97
Busy Restaurant or Canteen	65	Home Lawn Mower	98
Typing Pool (9 typewriters in use)	65	Turbine Condenser	98
Vacuum Cleaner in Private Residence (at 10 ft.)	69	150 cubic foot Air Compressor	100
		Banging of Steel Plate	104
Ringing Alarm Clock (at 2 ft.)	80	Air Hammer	107
		Jet Airliner (500 Ft. overhead)	115

These values are unlikely to be repeated as shown here and may vary by several decibels in similar situations. Reprinted by permission of Martin Hirschorn and *Sound and Vibration* (April, 1970)

However, because sound can set bodies vibrating, it can pack an incredible wallop. It can do work, it can produce heat, it can be reflected, bent, and absorbed.

Given the proper combination of acoustic energy and frequency, sound can destroy rock formations, mix paints, crack plaster, break windows, and wash dishes. In one classic experiment, exposure to intense sound lit a pipe and brewed a cup of coffee in seven minutes.

We live in a sea of sound waves, the vibrations of which may be as slow as three per second or as rapid as millions per second. The most familiar response to these vibrations is the sensation of hearing. Though the entire body "senses" the vibrations, the human sense of hearing responds only to the ones that fall within the range between 20 cycles per second to somewhere in the region of 15,000 cycles per second. (Remember, this is different from the decibel scale, which measures sound intensity, not frequency.) Below 20 cps is *infrasound*, sound of such low vibration it is inaudible though sensed as a vibration. Sound above 15,000 cps, called *ultrasound*, is inaudible to most people in industrialized countries.

We are able to "hear" because among the human senses is the ability to detect the very small and rapid fluctuations in the pressure of the air called sound waves. The detection apparatus is called the ear. It is this organ that first bears the brunt of acoustic abuse.

The basic hearing mechanism of the ear involves: the outer ear (external ear or pinna plus the external auditory canal), the middle ear, about one-third of an inch long (containing the familiar hammer, anvil, and stirrup bones), and the inner ear, a system of cavities lying within and protected by dense bone and containing the all-important cochlea. This apparatus must transmit to the brain an accurate pattern of all sound vibrations received from the environment. The human outer ear, from pinna to eardrum, is approximately four centimeters long. (The elephant's ear canal is eight inches long.) The middle ear has been described as so small it can be filled with five or six drops of water. The inner ear is no bigger than the tip of a little finger. All three parts together are approximately one and one-half inches long, an example of natural miniaturization. The outer ear serves as more than the collecting point for the sound waves. The ear canal can amplify the intensity of certain pitches by means of sympathetic resonance. This is one explanation for the amazing sensitivity of the ear to the sound vibrations. It's almost as if the ear had a hunger for sound, so great is its sensitivity.

Sound vibrations are condensed, and conducted by the ear canal to the eardrum, a membrane about one-forth of an inch in diameter. The resulting pulsations of the eardrum activate the three tiniest bones in the body, the malleus, incus, and stapes (more familiarly, the hammer, anvil, and stirrup). The three bones of the middle ear serve as a bridge between the eardrum and a membrane at the entrance to the inner ear (the oval window). The stapes, last link of the bony bridge, is attached to the oval window and causes it to vibrate. The vibrations of the oval window set up vibrations in the fluid in the two canals of the cochlea which surround the organ of Corti. Thus the three parts of the ear convert the mechanical waves of airborne sound energy into waves in liquid, and finally into electrical impulses.

It is in the cochlea of the inner ear that, via the all-important organ of Corti, conversion from mechanical to electrical energy takes place. Imbedded in the organ of Corti are some twenty to thirty thousand sensory cells, each of which is capped with fine hair, or cilia. Each hair cell of the inner ear responds only to a specific frequency. The cilia sensitive to high frequencies are at the beginning of the snail-like cochlea, and the low-frequency sensors are at the apex, or far end of the spiral.

Each hair is joined together with the others to become the auditory nerve. By some mechanism, not yet fully understood, the wave-like motion of the hair cells sets up a "coded" electrical signal that is transmitted to the auditory center of the brain.

Not all sound enters the body through the outer ear. The inner ear is capable of receiving acoustic energy via bone conduction and tissue conduction. Intense sound waves can penetrate the skull, the torso, and the groin.

To recognize a sound, the ear has to analyze millions of tones, each with a specific pitch and intensity. The American National Standards Institute defines pitch as "that attribute of auditory sensation in terms of which sounds may be ordered on a scale extending from low to high. Pitch depends primarily upon the frequency of the sound stimulus, but it also depends upon the sound pressure and wave form of the stimulus." Loudness is defined as "the intensive attribute of an auditory sensation in terms of which sounds may be ordered on a scale extending from soft to loud." Loudness is also influenced by the frequency of a sound and personal judgment of the listener.

Some sounds are pure tones; most are a combination of several tones. Many can best be described as "broad band" sounds; others as "narrow band" sounds. The whine of a jet is a narrow band sound.

The brain attempts to locate the source of a sound. The sightless human is helped in navigating his way by the echoes of sounds received from nearby reflecting surfaces such as walls and building exteriors.

The ear can hear the infinitesimal vibrations caused by a falling leaf and the vibrations caused by the intense sounds of a rocket engine, a range of about 150 decibels. The ear has been likened to an instrument which can measure in yards at one end of its range and yet detect changes of less than one-thousandth of an inch at the other end.

So sensitive is the human organism to sound that even the mere description of an unpleasant sound can evoke a physical response. Scratching a piece of hard chalk or a fingernail on a blackboard can give one goose pimples, and so can the description of such a sound source.

Sound evokes much more than the sensation of hearing. The sound signal is transmitted, via the brain, to almost every nerve center and organ of the body. Therefore, sound influences not only the hearing center of the brain, but the entire physical, physiological, emotional, and psychological makeup of the human being. The received sound wave evokes a combination of responses—auditory, intuitive, emotional, biological, associative. Sound's impact is a profound one.

The sound wave is both a message and a transmitter of mes-

sages. The message itself may be verbal or non-verbal. A verbal
sound signal may transmit a single fact: today is Monday. The
fact might be laden with significance and thus arouse emotion in
you: you have just lost your job. Non-verbal signals, such as
music, can also convey emotions. Non-verbal signals may also
cause irritating physiological and emotional states. In short,
sounds can make you ecstatically happy or terribly depressed.

Sound, per se, is a desirable and essential part of our lives and
of our environment. There are many sounds that are pleasant in
themselves; they can convey warmth and desired information.
Sound permits communication, the exchange of thoughts and
feelings between people. It enables us to enjoy the beauty of
music, the voices of nature: waterfalls, birds, the wind rustling
in trees, the ocean surf. It is a means of giving and receiving
life-saving warnings.

When does sound become noise?

There is no simple answer to this question, any more than
there is a simple answer to the question of what is an optimum
acoustic environment. We can only hope to approximate an
answer.

In general, sound is noise when its physical components disturb the relationship between man and his fellow man, and man
and his environment. Or, when the acoustic energy causes undue
stress and actual physiological damage.

In conventional terms, sound may be classified as noise when
it damages the hearing mechanism, causes other bodily effects
detrimental to health and safety, disturbs sleep and rest, interferes with conversation or other forms of communication, an-
noys or irritates.

Some authorities say that the most obvious effect of noise on
man is an interference with the ability to communicate. Sound
becomes noise when it masks sounds one wants to hear.
Nonetheless, this problem is not necessarily obvious to the victim as a *noise* problem.

"Speak up," judges often tell lawyers and witnesses. Sometimes this signifies a hearing problem on the judge's part; sometimes it means that outside noises are penetrating the halls of justice. A member of London's Scientific Advisory staff told me that one of the older judges came to him for a hearing test, explaining with embarrassment that he was having difficulty hearing his cases. Shortly thereafter another judge came up to the acoustic lab, and then another. Puzzled, the acoustic scientist did a noise level survey of the courtrooms, and discovered that speech was being masked by intrusive street noises.

Ironically, the masking effect of sound starts a spiral of other objectionable sounds. Fire and police departments, for example, justify making sirens louder and louder, to overcome increasingly higher street noises. Continuous masking is experienced in homes because of noisy air conditioners, appliances, and passing traffic, and perhaps this is one reason why neighbors play radios and TV at high volume.

One way of judging what noise does to behavior is by seeing what happens when it is removed. Researchers at the Ford Foundation's Educational Facilities Laboratories believe that disruptive noise influences both the dignity and the effectiveness of the teaching process. Donald Barr, headmaster of New York's Dalton School, has observed that 8- and 9-year-olds—noisy and unruly in the typical noise-box classroom—calmed down and concentrated in that school's first sound-treated classrooms. Noise and dignity seem interlinked.

Noise-induced hearing damage is described in Chapter 3.

Dr. Gunther Lehmann, former director of the Max Planck Institute, in Dortmund, West Germany, has warned that what threatens man is not the likelihood of auditory troubles or loss of hearing due to noise, "but an incessant disturbance, which under certain conditions creates an intolerable strain."

The effects of noise other than damage to hearing are called extra-auditory effects. Most of the science of acoustics has been applied to measuring only one category of extra-auditory response, described by the catch-all term of annoyance. Annoyance is probably the most widespread and one of the more complex responses to noise.

The acoustician approaches the annoyance reaction by attempting to separate the acoustic or physical factors (pitch, intensity, duration) from the extra-auditory factors. Of the acoustic factors, loudness has been selected as a key consideration. All other things being equal, the louder the sound, the more annoying it is. Loudness distracts. Loud shouting and yelling—from Indian war whoops to the Japanese banzai—have been used in battle to demoralize, confuse, and frighten.

Though loudness is related to the intensity of the sound, the more decibels the louder, other factors can influence loudness. For example, a given sound appears louder at night, if the background level is lower than during the day.

If one has been shielded from loud noise, sudden exposure is uncomfortable, and can prove startling. People who have had ear surgery find everyday noises inordinately discomfiting. Before the Belgian Congo got its independence, one of its government agencies placed an order for silencers for construction machines being shipped from Europe. It had been observed that Congolese workmen would run away from the construction sites because they could not stand the unmuffled noise.

Extremes of pitch are annoying. Illustrations are sirens (high pitch) and fog horns or boat whistles (low pitch). These intense sounds intrude over the background noise.

Annoyance appears to be a matter of degree and circumstance. For example, irregularity, lack of pattern, makes sound ugly and annoying. The unexpected, unpatterned sounds of jackhammers, auto horns, and helicopters cause unpleasant internal responses. Almost paradoxically, regularity, too, can irritate. The constant roar of an air compressor or a loud air conditioner is not soothing.

A sound which repeatedly changes its point of origin is annoying. When a noisy truck passes another vehicle on the highway, the overtaken driver is immersed in and consequently disoriented by the intense sound that seems to be coming from all directions at once.

Sounds can be annoying even if they are not loud. Proponents of center city heliports claim that helicopters are not as loud as jets, therefore not as annoying. But the distinctive drone and chop-chop of a helicopter is irritating. It is also terribly disturbing to have a relatively low-decibel background noise at night punctured by the clicking of heels on the floor overhead, the hammering in water pipes, the neighbor's TV.

Sound becomes noise for many non-acoustical reasons. Canned music in a restaurant or an elevator is noise to a man who is preoccupied. This is an invasion of privacy. According to the British Wilson Committee* annoyance can be "essentially the resentment we feel at an intrusion into the physical privacy which we have for the moment marked out as our own, or into our thoughts or actions."

The fight for a quieter world becomes obscured when feelings about a noise are divorced from the noise itself. We are told that how we react to a given noise may be influenced by our attitude towards the noise source, our state of health and well-being, our personalities, education, income, previous exposure, ad nauseum. Does the transportation noise problem disappear if we all learn to love driving and flying, or the industries that make these activities possible? Would I have been less disturbed by the subway project if I appreciated what the TA was doing for progress? Is a 90-decibel jackhammer really less of a noise because it takes place during the day, or because I've heard one before? It is relatively simple to measure the physical quality of the noise signal, its decibel level, frequency distribution, duration, number of occurrences per unit time, etc. It is virtually impossible to measure the significant human response to noise. Schemes for

*Noise—Final Report. Committee On The Problem Of Noise, Her Majesty's Stationery Office, London, 1964.

predicting complaints and evaluating annoyance responses are crude guidelines, their effectiveness questioned even by noise specialists.

A number of schemes have been developed to predict the response to a new noise in a given environment, or the response to a noise from a given source. According to acoustician Lew Goodfriend, "All currently used noise rating techniques are based not on what the optimum environment for man should be, but on what the public as a group will put up with."

One of these noise rating tools is the Composite Noise Rating, or CNR. It supposedly predicts whether a given noise will lead to no response, or provoke a rising degree of protest, culminating in vigorous legal action. "The objective," states Goodfriend, "is not to produce an enjoyable or even a suitable environment. It is merely to prevent complaints."

Another example of a noise rating system based on what people will tolerate is the family of "Noise Criteria" curves. Ratings obtained by means of these curves are aimed at "determining the *maximum level* of noise at which office personnel feel they can accomplish their duties without loss of efficiency." For secretarial areas (typing) and accounting areas (business machines), the recommended rating is NC-50 to NC-55. The environment for communication at this level is described as "unsatisfactory for conferences of more than two or three people; use of telephone slightly difficult; normal voice one to two feet; raised voice three to six feet."

Goodfriend is evolving a scheme using computers to obtain a statistical picture of the noise within a community. "From this information it should be possible by mathematical analysis to describe the optimum environment." Unfortunately for human beings, they do not lend themselves to formulae and equations.

We can measure sound; we can only guesstimate noise. But we know how to reduce noise and noise exposure (Chapter 8). Why not do so? Each day we avoid design for quiet we pay an unreasonable price for progress.

PART II

The Price Of Noise

CHAPTER THREE

The Price In Health

If ours were a civilized society, it would not be necessary to work so hard to make a case for noise as a health problem. But when courts rule that we must accept annoyance and even damage from noise as the price of civilization, a public health rationale for noise abatement becomes a must. And it is not easy to find one. People with limited foresight would like to wait until the blood comes out of the public's ears. To them noise is a necessary nuisance, and abatement is not entitled to a share of the nation's wealth. The same kind of limited viewpoint delayed action on air pollution until it had undeniably caused deaths in London, New York, Los Angeles, and Donora, Pennsylvania (where the relationship between air pollution and death was established for the first time). The challenge must emphasize the plausibility of harm.

What is health, anyway?

The traditional definition has been that health is freedom from disease. But health must include psychic health and the protection of the human personality. The World Health Organization codified these concepts in its constitution when it expanded the definition of health to include not only freedom from disease, but a state of well-being. This parallels the physician's growing recognition of the need for preventing disease—and not just waiting for illness to strike.

Acceptance of this progressive definition by organized medicine would give the physician a basis for supporting noise-abatement measures as a recognized method of disease prevention.

Diseases affecting the heart and the blood vessels—the cardiovascular diseases—cause the majority of deaths in the United States, the Soviet Union, and most other industrialized societies.

No one has yet established a direct relationship between noise and cardiovascular disease, and yet . . .

No less a physician than William H. Stewart, former Surgeon General of the United States Public Health Service, made this statement in his keynote address to the nation's first conference on noise as a health hazard:

"Donora incidents occur daily in communities across the U.S. Not in terms of specific numbers of deaths attributable to excessive noise exposure, but in terms of many more than 20 cardiovascular problems . . . for which the noises of twentieth-century living are a major contributory factor."

The most common and serious forms of organic heart disease are those affecting the coronary arteries which supply blood to the heart. When the passageway inside one of these vessels becomes sufficiently narrowed (atherosclerosis), or is blocked by a clot, a heart attack may occur. The cause of death is the reduction of the blood flow, and consequently the delivery of oxygen to the tissues. Without the necessary oxygen, the tissues die.

What causes the thickening of the arterial walls is the deposit of cholesterol and other fatty substances (serum lipids) that float in the blood. Though diet is popularly associated with increases in cholesterol levels, stress has been demonstrated to increase cholesterol and other fat levels and contribute to the thickening of the arterial walls. Stress increases the secretion of adrenalin, and this in turn increases the amount of free fatty acids in the blood stream, an increase associated with an elevation of cholesterol. It has been demonstrated at the University of South Dakota that noise levels common to the environment of man raise cholesterol levels in rats and rabbits (and also cause heart enlargement in rats). Dr. Samuel Rosen of CQC has stated that loud noises cause adrenal hormone to be released into the blood stream to intensify tension and arousal. Stress itself has been implicated as a primary reason for cholesterol changes.

Rosen warns, "We now have millions with heart disease, high blood pressure . . . who need protection from the additional stress of noise." In 1969 he told the Acoustical Society of America, "If a disorder such as atherosclerosis or coronary heart disease is present, [excessive] noise exposure could endanger health. . . ."

There are several suggested factors that increase the risk of an attack. When noise exerts an unfavorable influence over these factors, there is presumptive evidence that noise contributes in some degree to the chain of events leading to heart disease and to an eventual attack. Among these risk factors are cigarette smoking, overweight, lack of exercise. Of special interest is blood pressure.

Dr. Aram Glorig and other medical men have noted that blood pressure does go up with noise exposure. What happens if the noise exposure is continuous, and extends over a long period of time? Rosen, Gerd Jansen, and others have discovered that the impact on the peripheral blood vessels is a prolonged one, that the vasoconstriction (tightening of the blood vessels) persists for a significant length of time even after the noise is stopped. Not only does the vasoconstriction continue after the noise stops, the return to a normal state is slow.

The physical quality of the noise seems to be unimportant. The degree of vasoconstriction these physicians observed was the same for the noise of a punch press, an air pressure hammer, or white noise. (White noise is a "flat" noise with a more or less equal distribution of sound energy across the frequency spectrum.)

People with systemic weaknesses would react to vasoconstriction differently from normal, healthy persons. This suggests the possibility that people with systemic circulatory or cardiac disorders would be more grossly affected by noise.

According to Rosen, adrenalin increase, if chronic, could elevate blood pressure. Noise, hypertension, and heart disease thus make for a vicious circle: noise can elevate the blood pressure, elevated blood pressure can contribute to heart disease, and heart disease can be a cause of high blood pressure.

Rats subjected to excessive noise have developed hypertension, with the older rats showing the greatest sensitivity to noise stress. As for humans, it does not require a sonic boom to trigger a sudden, potentially damaging increase in cerebral blood pressure. In one test, a popping paper bag raised the brain pressure more quickly than a hypodermic injection.

Disordered heart beats may be the central problem in at least 40 per cent of sudden heart-attack deaths, and they trigger most of the deaths during the first four days after an attack. Noise influences the heart's beat. Experimental work in the Soviet Union has shown a weakening of the contractions of the heart muscle from noise exposure. Many Russian workers exposed to continuous noise between 85 and 120 dB complained of chest pain, and medical examination of these workers revealed irregularities of the heart beat. Russian research shows that workers in high-noise ball bearing and steel plants have a high incidence of irregularities in heart rate, which in some cases can be fatal.

A town in New Jersey moved a firehouse siren away from the adjacent home of a boy with congenital heart disease after his doctor warned that the noise could throw him into a spasm that could be fatal.

In caring for the total person, doctors have recognized that noise hinders recuperation by interfering with rest. The medical profession intuitively urges adequate rest and sleep for patients recuperating from acute illness or surgery. Questions are currently being asked about the impact of noisy hospitals on coronary patients. Physicians now wish to put their intuitively wise judgment on a firmer basis. At Columbia Presbyterian Medical Center in New York City, it was demonstrated that one of the reasons patients couldn't rest after open-heart surgery was the acoustical environment: they spent three to five days in a tile-lined recovery room "surrounded by a monotonous hissing noise." Insiders long have referred to hospitals as "acoustical torture chambers."

In 1963 the Public Health Service reported that "hospital patient rooms are noisier than most residential sleeping areas in cities or suburbs. The noise levels in a typical patient room are above those recommended for sleeping areas in residences."

"Quiet, Hospital" signs do not apply to jets, jackhammers, and trucks.

There are times when hospitals are so noisy that doctors are forced to take unnecessary and undesirable X-rays because they cannot use the stethoscope for diagnosis. Patients are sometimes given sleeping pills just to keep them from complaining about slamming doors, dropped bedpans, staff conversations, shrill telephone bells, and data-stamping machines in the nurses' stations.

If noise reduces chances of survival—and can be controlled, doctors are saying—why not control it and increase the chances of survival? This is easier said than done, but some first steps are being taken. The National Heart Institute is sponsoring an $11-million study to investigate the best environmental conditions for patients' rooms, including optimum levels of sound. Someday the environment inside an ambulance will be investigated, and that investigation will be the beginning of the end of today's strident sirens.

After he leaves the hospital, the patient's home becomes the focus for recuperation. Dr. Christiaan Barnard, the heart transplant pioneer, noted the relationship between recuperation and noise in the home when he made arrangements for a silencing device for Dr. Blaiberg's family telephone.

Can noise cause a heart attack? Probably not directly. Can noise contribute to heart disease and create an environment hostile to recovery? The answer seems to be yes. The millions of Americans with diagnosed or suspected heart disease would seem to have a stake in noise abatement.

It can be taken for granted that to be awakened is disturbing. But what about those more frequent cases where there is noise intrusion, yet the sleeper sleeps on. Progress without price? Doctors are not so sure.

Starting about ten years ago, doctors began scientific studies of sleep. They discovered that we sleep in repeated cycles ranging from a shallow level to a deep level. They were even able to detect the all-important dream state, the REM (Rapid Eye Movement). Each level apparently contributes to the restorative function of sleep. For sleep to perform its restorative function, each sleeper must experience the complete sleep cycle, with the requisite number of minutes in each stage.

According to one Swiss medical researcher, Dr. H. R. Richter, "For complete recovery during the night and to guarantee full efficiency at work during the next day one needs six to eight hours of undisturbed sleep with approximately 1 to 1½ hours of dream state."

Without awakening the sleeper, noise stimuli will constrict his blood vessels, change his heart rate and muscular tone.

The effect of noise during sleep can be recorded and analyzed. To find out what noise does to the sleep stages, investigators use the electroencephalogram (EEG) to record the patterns of brain waves during sleep. According to Dr. Richter the EEG is the technique of choice for investigations into the question of whether traffic noise does affect the central nervous system, even when people imagine they have slept well and do not remember the nightly disturbances.

Noise does not have to be anywhere near a deafening 85 decibels to disturb the sleep stages. Even noise of a low intensity produces arousal reactions, and what is significant, prevents the sleeper from reaching the deep sleep stage.

Canadian researchers have sought a correlation between the noise level of a passing vehicle and the extent of arousal. Observations of changes in the brain wave patterns have shown that the deep sleep stage can be cut short by the passing of a single truck. The Canadian National Research Council's studies showed that some subjects may awaken "more than 50 per cent of the time at a peak noise level of the passing truck of 50 decibels. . . . At 70 decibels the most probable reaction is to awaken. . . ." Some sources recommend that interiors of bedrooms not exceed 30 or 35 decibels. The fact that such relatively low noise levels can so profoundly influence the sleeping state takes on great significance when one realizes that transportation modes and air conditioners expose millions of sleeping people to levels of 50 decibels and much higher.

According to Dr. Richter, the number of disturbances during the night may be even more important than the intensity of the noise. He observes that motor vehicles on expressways, which now are almost as busy at night as during the day, can disturb a sleeper at the rate of once every few seconds. He notes that the sleeper does not get used to irregular stimuli of short duration.

Summarizing the work of other investigators, he further states: "Sleep deprivation leads to psychic alterations, as irritability, tiredness, delirious and even paranoic states. Among others West and colleagues have studied the psychosis of sleep deprivation. They even suggest that long-term sleep deprivation may cause irreversible changes in the nervous system. Hartmann recently emphasized that most probably the lack of dreamstate is the main factor for these psychic abnormalities."

Studies have been made of prisoners subjected to "brainwashing." Extreme sleep deprivation created physical sensations such as itching and blurred vision, and mental symptoms ranging from mild memory lapses to hallucinations and actual psychoses. In a paper presented at the 1965 annual meeting of the Association for Research in Nervous and Mental Diseases, Dr. Louis J. West, Director of the Psychiatry Department of the University of Oklahoma, observed that during the Korean War, Air Force prisoners who gave false confessions had been awakened at irregular intervals and allowed to sleep only in snatches.

One reason the full impact of noise on civilian sleep and health has not been thoroughly examined is probably that patients suffering from subclinical sleep deprivation syndromes usually do not relate such vague symptoms as aches and pains, headaches, fatigue, visual disturbances, poor concentration, apathy and depression to disturbed sleep. Neither do these types of symptoms necessarily drive them to the doctor. If they do, unless the doctor is given information with which to understand the patient's sleep environment, *he* may not relate the symptoms to sleep deprivation, according to Dr. West.

The problem is that since the sleep-deprived individual is generally able to perform standard tasks and otherwise give the appearance of good health, the subtle effects of mild subclinical sleep deprivation syndrome go unnoticed. These include "subtle impairment of creative thinking, of imaginative and original approaches to the challenges of everyday life, of vigorous solutions to complex problems and other manifestations of the highest integrative neuro-biological functions." It would seem that long-term impairment of such abilities would be undetectable on the basis of a single test measurement, yet might be open to detection if performance levels were compared over a long period of time. This is another area in which research is needed.

In considering sleep deprivation, account must be taken of the impact of forcing *everybody* to wake up at 7:00 A.M., the typical hour for the beginning of legal noise nuisance. Doctors are beginning to find out that, metabolically, there actually are two types of individuals, day people and night people. Since each individual has his own sleep-waking rhythm, to force a "night person" to wake at a fixed hour in the morning is to deprive him of sleep. The forced loss of an hour's sleep in the morning may cause a number of internal physiological reactions that make the victim start his day tense and tired, observed Dr. A. Huwiler at the Baden-Baden meeting. Patients of his who lived near the Zurich airport were being awakened by the early-morning idling of aircraft. Dr. Huwiler acknowledged that there is no scientific proof of the connection between airport noise and patients' symptoms of fatigue, heart and circulatory changes, and the like, but he believes there is a good case for probability. Must we not find out?

Difficulty in falling asleep is associated with tension, resentment, or frustration. Noise may contribute to any or all of these emotional states. Dr. Edward F. Crippen, Deputy Health Commissioner of Detroit assigned to investigate that city's 1967 riots, suggested to the 95th Annual Meeting of the American Public Health Association that part of the tension found in ghettoes may be attributable to interrupted sleep. "The din of the modern city," he said, includes "noises far above levels for optimum sleeping. Result: insomnia and instability."

One side effect of sleep deprivation is the resort to sleeping pills. "The use of, and addiction to sleep-inducing pills," states Dr. Richter, "has become a psychiatric problem of our modern times." Sleeping pills can be a harmful solution. Dr. West, who urges caution in the use of drugs for sleeping, has observed that true sleep must be distinguished from "barbiturate stupor." Some types of sleeping pills in themselves modify the natural sleep stages.

"Of all effects of noise," concluded England's conservative

Wilson Committee, "repeated interference with sleep is least to be tolerated because prolonged loss of sleep is known to be injurious to health."

Years ago, investigators were looking for a standardized stressing agent, something that would consistently cause abnormalities in animals. By accident they discovered that noise could produce the abnormalities they wanted: lesions in the urinary and cardiovascular systems, changes in the uteri and ovaries of female animals, alterations in the testicular structure of male animals. They also discovered that the acoustic stimulus could cause changes in the body's chemistry: an increased production of adrenal hormones, a decreased production of ovarian hormones, and other complex hormonal changes that influence fertility, growth, and other essential bodily functions.

Dr. Hans Selye pioneered a theory that the body produced these complex chemical changes to enable it to cope with stress. This stress reaction he described as the body's normal adjustment to an abnormal situation. However, when the stress is constant or too intense, the defense reaction itself becomes sufficiently extreme to be harmful. The adrenal glands become enlarged, the lymph tissues shrink, the stomach and intestines develop bleeding ulcers. He discovered that in patients who were under stress or tension from various sources, there appeared a number of vague, diffuse symptoms such as aches and pains, coated tongue, fever, and mental confusion.

Describing Dr. Selye's work, *Saturday Review* editor Norman Cousins wrote, "He has studied the effects of anxiety, stress and exhaustion on the adrenal glands. He reports a direct physiological connection between persistent tension and fear and the weakening of the total human organism. What happens, he finds, is that the supply of adrenalin runs dry and the body loses its chemical balance, or homeostasis. . . . The effects of adrenal exhaustion vary all the way from physical crippling to heart disease."

Dr. Selye believes we are born with a limited amount of adaptation energy and that aging is a depletion of that energy. This could mean that excessive stress shortens life. And the Metropolitan Life Insurance Company, with an economic stake in longevity, says that one of the damaging side effects of stress is that it "may lead to disease, cause us to age prematurely, or sometimes even shorten life."

Certain diseases are designated as stress-activated diseases: the coronary, the ulcer, the irritable colon, the erratic blood pressure, the migraine headache, a great deal of mental illness, and what one doctor describes as "Selye's syndrome of 'just being sick.'"

When chickens are stressed with noise a complex physiological change takes place. Air-ground military maneuvers in the midst of North Carolina's largest poultry counties provided the necessary evidence. Chicken houses were subjected to the noises from planes, trucks, tanks, and foot traffic. "The roar of the motors and rotors combined with dust and air movement seemed most effective in exciting the hens," reported Dr. Douglas Hamm, poultry scientist. Egg production was down.

No one bothered to check for hearing damage among the chickens. It was assumed that the stress had its major effect on the central nervous system and hormonal system. While this is granted to chickens, it is not granted to humans, who must show hearing loss before others will accept the idea that noise has impaired their functioning.

Granted that a certain amount of stress is normal, and needed for survival, what happens when we ring the alarm bell too often?

Day and night, urban man's nervous system is getting false alarms from sirens, helicopters, jets, trucks, cars, motorcycles, with and without defective mufflers. The constant rain of noise can cause a state of stress. Ecologist Dr. Bruce Welch compares being forced to live in an environment of constant high-level stimulation to driving at high speed in second gear, or maybe in first. At the very least, a lot of energy is wasted, rejecting and reacting to unwanted sounds of excessive amplitude.

If the body is preoccupied with defending itself against constant physical and psychological stresses, its biological resistance to disease is lowered.

It should be noted that the diseases of yesterday—scarlet fever, polio, diphtheria—have given place to the unsolved problems of the chronic diseases such as arthritis, rheumatism, diabetes, cancer, cardiovascular diseases. Many of these diseases, incidentally, do not exist in the relatively noise- and other stress-free environment of primitive societies.

Urban man suffers from a host of ailments the causes of which are unknown, but for which rest and freedom from tension, both to prevent an attack and to prevent a recurrence, are prescribed.

One indication of the impact of noise on the nervous system is the fact that epileptic seizures are sometimes triggered by noises. It would seem more than coincidental that on October 16, 1966, the medicine section of *The New York Times* carried one story captioned "It's getting noisier," and next to it another, "Epilepsy on the rise." Noisy cities must be quite a tribulation to epileptics.

Dr. Jansen's studies at the Max Planck Institute have shown that noise bursts of 70 decibels and more caused pronounced bodily reactions which, he believes, could lead to illness if continued and high. In his pioneering study of a thousand steel workers, the group working in noisy conditions—more than 90 decibels—had a higher incidence of physiological and psychological disturbances than a comparable group working under quiet conditions (61 per cent as against 48 per cent). The noise-stressed group also revealed a 24 per cent incidence of heart irregularities as against 16 per cent for the "quiet" group. In Dr. Jansen's opinion, many industrial noise levels cause such undesirable reactions.

Among the acousticians who have noted a possible relationship between stressful noise and physiological damage is Los Angeles physicist Dr. Vern Knudsen, who has been studying and working with sound for some forty years. "I have always been sensitive to noise," he says, "and I even believe, though I have no proof, that my reactions to noise were significant in developing a series of ulcers in my duodenum. I knew that sudden noises cause violent stomach contractions, and I am convinced these contractions can exacerbate incipient peptic ulcers."

Dr. Knudsen is a physicist. What do physicians think about noise and ulcers? I once got into a heated argument with a doctor with whom I was associated on a noise-abatement panel. I did not want his medical report to place annoyance as the least important of the effects of noise, at least not without some disclaimer that annoyance did not mean inconsequential nuisance. The doctor was disturbed because he felt I was asking him to make statements about noise that were not scientifically supportable. However, he made this private admission: "I have had patients with ulcers. I knew in my heart that noise played a part, but I couldn't say anything about it. I couldn't prove it."

A Department of Agriculture review of animal studies reported experiments in which rats exposed to noise showed changes in the lining of the stomach, changes that could cause the appearance of gastric ulcers. Ten minutes of exposure to 80 decibels of noise followed by a twenty-minute quiet period produced a 37 per cent reduction in the number of contractions of the stomach. A noise intensity of 60 decibels or more reduced the secretion of saliva by about 44 per cent and also reduced the flow of gastric juices. Permanent abnormalities in such bodily functions can lead to more permanent types of injury, such as intestinal ulcers.

Diseases related to stress cannot be effectively controlled in a non-quiet environment. Arthritis seems to be one such disease.

No one knows the cause of arthritis. It can develop, according to the Arthritis Foundation, when there has been no injury, no overwork of the joint, no infection. Worry and fatigue may increase the severity of the symptoms. Many patients notice the beginning of rheumatoid arthritis symptoms following a disturbing experience. University of Rochester medical researchers have reported that rheumatoid arthritis victims had stressful experiences preceding an attack.

Though freedom from noise is never mentioned, woven in and out of the program for the prevention and cure of arthritis is rest, rest for the inflamed joint, rest for the whole body, generally in bed. The treatment for acute attacks of rheumatic fever includes rest. I wonder what it was like to have arthritis on upper Sixth Avenue?

Too much annoyance prevents the body from simmering down after stimulation. According to Dr. Etienne Grandjean of Zurich's Federal Institute of Technology, interference with the body's recovery processes is the main reason underlying subjective annoyance. From this point of view, annoyance must be considered a biological protective mechanism helping man to avoid noise and to secure needed recovery. The biological meaning of annoyance is therefore comparable to other feelings of discomfort like hunger, fatigue, cold or heat—all of which are life-protecting warnings.

Some doctors regard noise-induced annoyance as potentially harmful. Doctors associated with the German Medical Information Service recognize that circumstances dictate whether or not a given noise annoyance is a mere nuisance or a health problem.

Noise annoyance can be a health problem if:

1. The victim is a night worker who must sleep days;
2. The victim is doing mental or creative work;
3. The victim is ill, or convalescing.

To be dismissed as merely an innocent irritant, noise must be brief, not too loud, occur only during normal daytime periods, and be of a specific quality and type. However, what may be mildly or non-irritating to most, may be annoying to the sick or the convalescent. Psycho-physical distractions due to noise may be cause for legal redress where work is primarily mental and creative.

If noise stress activates the biological organism to seek quiet, what happens when that need cannot be met? A person can do something about hunger, thirst, and fatigue. But what happens if he can't avoid noise?

Perhaps the unmet urge for escape is responsible for the acts of violence triggered by noise. Extreme hunger and thirst have forced men to behave irrationally. Is it not conceivable that unrelenting noise may also produce acts of violence?

Most noise victims, however, do not give vent to their anger. And since they usually have no rights against the noise source, they turn their rage inward. Or, even if there is no conscious awareness of the irritation, the organism is tensed.

One result of unreleased tension may be headaches. The modern incidence of headaches is associated with industrialization. Some experts believe New York has the highest headache rate in the United States. Dr. Arnold P. Friedman, a psychiatrist-neurologist who runs the headache unit at Montefiore Hospital, New York City, believes that tension, or "nerves," accounts for 70 per cent of the headaches which are so severe they annually send 24 million Americans to doctors for help.

A sudden rise in blood pressure may cause a headache.

Noise causes a sudden rise in blood pressure.

Headache pain may be caused by contraction of the head and neck muscles in response to stress.

Noise causes stress.

Many headaches occur when the blood vessels around the brain swell and impinge on a sensitive nerve, or when the blood supply to the brain is choked off by tense neck muscles. The muscle tension constricts the arteries, and the subsequent dilating phase is the painful phase.

Noise tenses muscles.

Migraine headaches are most often triggered by emotional factors in persons whose blood vessels are predisposed to painful changes in diameter.

Noise changes the diameter of the blood vessels.

Can noise cause headaches? No one knows, but it seems plausible that a dose of quiet could hurt aspirin sales.

It should not be surprising that the repeated acoustic shocks of appliances and transportation produce tension. It is as if the response to each unexpected signal were that of a total alert, with the body responding with maximum preparation for the unexpected.

This is how Dr. Welch describes the reaction of the brain to sudden sound: "Your ears register the sound and you whirl about, eyes seeking the cause. . . . That brief moment in which you heard, turned, and saw launched a whirlwind of activity. 'Messages' flashed over a complicated nerve net to and from the brain. Chemicals in the brain flowed and changed. Simultaneously the other events around you triggered similar developments in the brain."

It would also seem that noise produces tension because it violates the "zones of sensory experience" described by anthropologist Dr. Edward T. Hall. Certainly noise is a trespass of the "social zone" four to ten feet from the body, and a trespass of the "personal zone" a little more than arm's length. But it seems to me that what makes noise so unendurable is that it also violates the "intimate zone," the one associated with lovemaking, comforting, and protecting.

Given all of this, there is good reason to suspect that in addition to chemical and physical reactions, noise plays havoc with our minds and our emotions. It is difficult to believe that noise which irritates, disturbs sleep, and constantly jars our nerves, just goes in one ear and out the other.

Until recently doctors have resisted the idea that emotions can play a role in all diseases, including infections, cancer, and heart ailments. Now the medical profession is receiving a flow of research reports that establish a relationship between emotions and disease. Emotional disturbance was reported to influence the common cold, attacks of asthma, and even the state of one's gums. (Yes, dentists are being urged to include some psychology as part of their treatment.) Other medical researchers have suggested a link between emotional states and the ability to ward off disease states, or get well once an illness has developed.

Ashley Montagu develops an interesting hypothesis that the emotions of the mother are directly communicated to the unborn child. Her emotions increase the hormonal output in her bloodstream and this increase is transmitted to the child's bloodstream. Severe emotional upsets at a critical development period might, he believes, be harmful.

One of the more striking papers presented at the December 1969 meeting of the American Academy for the Advancement of Science was that by Lester W. Sontag, M.D. on noise as a threat to the fetus. Enough research has been done, reported Dr. Sontag, to indicate that the embryo is vulnerable to environmental stresses, including sound pollutants. He cautions that the unborn be protected from excessive noise exposure.

Research is needed comparing the number of still-births and congenital deformities among children of mothers living in noise-stressed sites, such as airport vicinities, and mothers living in quiet locales.

A new hypothesis of annoyance is suggested by the work of Jansen and Rosen. Annoyance could be the reaction of the body to momentary "dying" of essential organs and tissues temporarily deprived of their normal flow of blood by noise-induced vasoconstriction.

What does vasoconstriction mean?

During the period when the blood vessels constrict there is a diminution of blood in circulation. Constriction slows the flow of blood through the vessels and therefore less oxygen and other nutrients reach an area at any given moment. The "pins and needles" feeling in a finger around which a rubber band has been tightened is a good example of what happens when there is an interference with normal blood flow.

Dr. Lehmann has reported that exposure to loud noise in factories interferes with blood circulation, and that workers in a boiler factory suffered constantly from impaired circulation in the skin. Vasoconstriction and accompanying loss of oxygen and other nutrients may be a cause of destruction of the cells of hearing, as well as of cells in other organs of the body.

If vasoconstriction from acoustic insults could eventually lead to a chronic state of constriction, and the cells of the inner ear eventually succumb, why may it not be assumed that some kind of damage is being done to many tissues and organs of the body if they, too, suffer from repeated vasoconstriction?

This theory of choking of the vital organs of the body would establish a physiological basis for annoyance. It would also explain why there are variations in individual reaction. The choking-off of the organ varies in proportion to the intensity, duration, suddenness, and repetition of the stimulus. One incident of stimulus can be so mild it passes unnoticed; a little more choking, and the victim develops a mild sense of annoyance; repeated choking with acute blood and oxygen stoppage, and the discomfiture increases and rises to intolerable levels. Choke an internal organ long enough, or severely enough, and it dies, as seems to have been demonstrated with the cells in the inner ear. Is it not possible that the subjective feeling of annoyance is, at least in part, caused by the "choking" of the various organs and tissues of the body by depriving them of a normal supply of blood?

Research is needed, such as that suggested by Dr. Rosen, which would attempt to correlate noise, vasoconstriction, and the subjective feeling of annoyance. This vasoconstriction theory raises the concept of annoyance to a level at which applied research would seem possible and fruitful. There may be a discernible biological and physiological basis for annoyance.

How often does one hear this statement: "At first the noise bothered me, but I got used to it."

But what the speaker means is only that his conscious awareness was reduced or disappeared altogether. One does not get used to noise. Somewhere in the human body, that sound is being absorbed—at an as yet unknown price. This is the law of the conservation of energy. Energy does not just disappear.

Whether or not noise annoyance is a health problem depends, to some degree, on the price to the human organism of "adapting," of making the necessary adjustments to an abnormal situation.

In 1966, Karl D. Kryter, who does research for NASA and the FAA at the Stanford Research Institute, reported: "There is evidence that following an initial adjustment to and learning the nature and meaning of one's noise environment people become less, rather than more, tolerant of continued exposure to aircraft noise."

In examining the question of adaptation, some researchers distinguish between exposure to meaningful and meaningless sounds. Meaningful noise is the noise that contains information. To Dr. Jansen for example, "It seems that man gets accustomed to most of the meaningful auditory stimuli if they are repeated often." Even then, he cautions, "scientific research now is not yet able to give all the criteria needed to determine the point at which health is endangered by a meaningful noise." According to Dr. Jansen, the personality of the listener, his individual physiological and psychological makeup, and his life experiences, all determine how well he becomes accustomed to meaningful noises. This is evident in the varying responses one gets when a group of people are exposed to construction noise. Some are more capable of tolerating it than others. But this does not necessarily mean they are not reacting to some component of that noise.

"The most dangerous noise," states Jansen, "is noise we are accustomed to, that we do not 'hear,' such as traffic noises. These are the noises that cause physiological responses because of their intensities or frequency-ranges. They do not lend themselves to adaptation." Jansen is quite concerned about the impact of this noise to which the person is accustomed but which does not convey information. Such a sound can be the constant roar of traffic that becomes, for some, an unnoticed part of the environment. Air conditioner noise is another example. Such meaningless noises starting at 70 decibels stimulate the vegetative nervous system, the stimulation increasing with intensity and other physical characteristics of the acoustic energy.

Jansen and Rosen observed that "white noise," noise without any predominantly strong tones, at 90 decibels, approximately the level found in some subways, caused the pupil of the eye to dilate, blood volume in the skin to be reduced because of vasoconstriction, a decrease in the stroke volume of the heart, and an increase of diastolic blood pressure. The increase in diastolic pressure, however, disappeared sometimes after several months of exposure.

In a classic study conducted over a three-year period with the same students of a pedagogic academy, Dr. Jansen was able to substantiate his evaluation of the adaptive process. Most of the students were exposed every day during their three years at the academy. Whether the noise burst was in milliseconds, or 90 minutes long, the subjects consistently reacted with vasoconstriction. The vasoconstrictive effect lasted as long as the stimulation; years of stimulus repetition failed to produce any signs of adaptation. "The noise-induced vegetative reaction," reports Dr. Jansen, "was always the same within the whole period."

Can this failure to adapt, which means that the body gets thrown on the alert with each noise burst, cause harm? Says Dr. Jansen, "These reactions caused by noise up to 95 dB must not be regarded as pathological when the noise is applied once or a few times; they might be pathological when a man is influenced for long years with intensities more than 95 dB (as investigations of industrial workers have proved). If there is an additional factor (psychic or somatic), it might be possible to endanger human health with less intensities and shorter time."

This last point is important. There is a tendency to dismiss noises found in the everyday environment as unimportant because they usually are below such intensities and in many cases are of short duration. There is also a tendency to evaluate noise exposure as if the person so exposed was in perfect health and not undergoing any other intense stresses. An organ forced to adapt to one set of abnormal conditions may have difficulty adapting to another set of abnormal conditions. Scientific research has not yet come up with an exact limit at which health becomes endangered.

Another view is presented by Dr. Bruce Welch, who specializes in investigations of stress and brain chemistry:

"It is often said that we 'adapt' to much stimuli, but this is simply not true if by 'adapt' one means to become just as well off as before. At the cognitive level, we come to be somewhat less surprised by loud noises after being subjected to them for a time. But we never cease to be startled. Instead of 'adapt,' a better word might be 'enured.' At the physiological level, we cease to recognize sounds of some intensities at all, and we cease to respond quite so violently to those which do affect us. This, however, as we have seen, simply reflects the fact that our nervous system is maintained at a higher level of activation, or adjusted to a higher balance-point in the interplay between activating and inhibitory neural systems all of the time."

I asked Dr. Welch if his view of adapting would apply to a sound stimulus from something like a STOLcraft, and he replied in the affirmative: "The addition of such intrusive sounds [helicopters and STOLcraft] to those with which the populace is already obliged to contend will weight the emotional and physiological balances further towards the extreme of sensory overloading and the debilitating effects which it may produce."

Most research has been done on the effects of industrial noise, not the variegated cacophony of today's civilized living. Is there periodicity or rhythm in the auto horn, the helicopter flyover, the jet flyover, the blender, the lawn mower, the garbage truck? All are sudden, unexpected. Adjustment does not seem possible.

If body tissue is penetrated by a needle with a given force, the pain decreases with repeated jabbing. Does the decline or even the absence of pain mean there is no tissue damage? Isn't the human nervous system being poked with the broad-band noise of an air conditioner, the sharp whine of a garbage truck, the staccato interjection of a jackhammer? To live with noise is not unlike living with electric shocks.

"Adapting" in any case to a continuing abnormal situation is like living with a bad marriage. Certainly a mismated couple scraping on each other's nerves can "adapt" and continue living together. What is the price of that adaptation, both to the partners and to the children of such a family, and to the community? What decibel formula measures adapting?

At certain intense levels small animals have been killed by noise exposure. The original rat-killing *cum* intense sound experiment was performed in a laboratory with a special sound generator. However, Albert Hoeffleur, a Swiss delegate to the 1966 AICB congress, told me he had witnessed the killing of a rat by noise in a real-life situation. The rodent was held in the stream of a jet engine. In fifteen minutes the animal was dead.

The intense sound energy was trapped in the furry hide, and cooked the animal to death. Which should be of some consolation to bald-headed men. Except that though the lethal exposure for man is greater than that for small animals, 150-160 decibels can destroy hearing.

In another animal experiment, rats were exposed to an air blast for from five to ten minutes a day, every weekday for from 15½ weeks to 124 weeks. Almost all showed dilated pupils and increased frequency of urination and defecation. Another reaction observed was a frenzied running attack in which the rat ran and leaped rapidly about the pen. In most cases this attack was ended by a series of convulsions and a final 3-5 minute state of tonic rigidity often so marked that the extremities "were able to be molded into bizarre positions." In most cases, rats did not die after these attacks. According to the February 1945 *American Journal of Physiology,* they only suffered.

Granted these are animal experiments. But we cannot ignore the report of human beings who worked in the close vicinity of high-performance jet engines during development and maintenance periods. These men were said to have developed diarrhea, nausea, giddiness, and in extreme cases if the exposure was prolonged, spontaneous pneumothorax. At first food poisoning was suspected, since the engineers involved were wearing protective earmuffs. The cause apparently was the intense sound energy which penetrated their skulls and torsos. True, these are intense noises, but without any effective anti-noise restrictions, there is nothing to protect the people who work in proximity to jet development.

Most of the preceding discussion has concerned audible sound. Sounds above and below the audible range also influence the living organism. To keep rats and other rodents away from flour mills, bakeries, and restaurants, use is being made of a sound-generating device called the Pied-Piper. This produces an intense ultrasonic sound said to be audible only to rodents, and acts as a repellent.

We know too little about the effect of ultrasound on humans. Even the term is used loosely, and some sounds called ultrasonic are actually audible. The piercing whistle of the "ultrasonic tooth cleaner" and sonic remote-control switches for television sets are cases in point. Public health authorities should be investigating the escalating use of ultrasonics in surgery, in medical diagnostics, and in appliances.

Military research for new weapons has led to the discovery that very low frequency sound can cause a profound disturbance inside the human body. An article in the London *Sunday Times* of April 16, 1967, reported that French scientists were working on infrasound as an acoustic weapon. These investigators discovered that vibrations of less than 10 cps (human hearing starts at 16-20 cps) create a pendulum reaction within the body that can be built up to intolerable intensities. The sensation of infrasound is similar to that experienced when one is exposed to the low-pitched horn of an ocean liner. During their researches, the investigators suffered internal pain from vibrations induced in the stomach, heart, and lungs. Their subjective reaction was described as a rubbing between the various organs because of a sort of resonance.

Infrasound investigators at the University of Illinois noted that since antiquity there have been reports that changes in barometric pressure and other weather factors accompanied behavioral problems ranging from suicide attempts to forgetfulness and malaise. They studied the sound waves produced by tornadoes, severe storms, winds, earthquakes, and volcanic activity.

Selecting two behavioral items—automobile accident rates and the rate of absenteeism among school children—they sought for a correlation between these two phenomena and naturally-occuring infrasonic waves. They did find a statistically significant relationship between the presence of strong infrasonic waves, generated by natural phenomena, and the behavior being studied. In the laboratory, infrasonic waves produced disturbances that might increase driver-responsible auto accidents, and generalized symptoms that would keep children home from school. Infrasonics has as yet been little explored, and these preliminary findings warrant detailed study.

For giving us speed and convenience, technology demands part, and sometimes all, of our sense of hearing.

It comes as a surprise to many that noise can cause deafness: not the trauma of an explosion, but the cumulative effect of prolonged exposure to noise below the levels produced by the

Chicago and New York subway systems. This kind of noise exposure is deafening millions in industry, and unknown numbers on farms and in offices.

Hearing loss from noise exposure is called sensory-neural or nerve deafness. The effect is to disable the inner ear and prevent it from transmitting sound signals to the brain. Though damage to the organ of hearing is the one form of bodily harm that can be measured, to a degree, and viewed under the microscope, very little is known about the exact mechanism by which the sound-wave pressure destroys the ear.

There are no direct tests for measuring the destructive effect of noise. Not even hearing loss can be measured directly. The tuning fork can detect the ability to hear specific frequencies. The varieties of audiometers measure the ability to understand selected speech signals or the ability to detect a pure tone of select frequencies. In pure-tone testing each tone is presented to the listener in a variety of ascending and descending intensities until it is determined at what decibel level the listener responds. In other words, pure-tone testing measures the range of select frequencies which can be heard, and the intensity—measured in decibels—necessary for the signal to be heard.

Only a periodic series of hearing tests can detect the onset of hearing loss.

Dr. Rosen has postulated that one reason for nerve deafness is reduction of the blood supply to the nerve endings of the inner ear. Hardening of the arteries could be one reason for the reduced blood supply; vasoconstriction caused by noise could be another. In 1961, together with an international team of physicians and audiologists, Rosen conducted a study of the primitive Mabaans of the African Sudan. These people were found to have a keen sense of hearing and no evidence of coronary heart disease. They live in an environment almost free of noise—the typical level is 40 decibels—with few emotional stresses. There was evidence that their blood vessels enjoyed a normal elasticity even in old age. Industrialized man loses this elasticity; hardening occurs. Among the Mabaans, who live in an atmosphere of virtual silence, the hearing of even men in their seventies and eighties is the equal of healthy youngsters of ten.

Noise-stressed blood vessels that have lost their elasticity take a long time to return to normal size after the noise stimulus is removed. This means that the blood flow is diminished for a period long enough to cause damage to the cells fed by the circulatory system. Rosen suggested that continued exposure to excessive noise may eventually lead to a chronic state of blood deprivation and finally to death of the cells involved with hearing.

This scientific hypothesis has since been substantiated in work on monkeys. At the University of Michigan, monkeys were subjected to a noise signal and then put to death. It was found that the inner ear had indeed been damaged, and that the blood vessels were constricted.

Another theory for the cause of hearing loss is that the constant pressure of intense noise does physical damage to the nerve endings in the inner ear. The concept is analogous to the case of wear and tear on the pile of a rug.

In any event, noise can produce what ear specialists call a threshold shift, or hearing loss.

Even a few minutes of exposure to intense noise can cause temporary deafness. The users of noisy appliances, powered lawn mowers for example, experience significant hearing loss for a variable period of time after using such products. This loss is called noise-induced temporary threshold shift, or NITTS. NITTS is what the members of rock'n'roll bands experience wherever amplified music is played. Subjectively it may be observed as a muffled sensation and/or a ringing in the ears. One empirical method of detecting a NITTS is to listen to the mechanism of a watch before and after exposure. The degree of loss is indicated by the amount of time needed for recovery.

Researchers at the University of Minnesota measured hearing sensitivity of band members following a four-hour session of music having an over-all sound-pressure level ranging from 110 to 125 decibels. In 25 minutes there was a loss of from 10 to 30 decibels of hearing in the critical 2,000 cps speech frequency. Recovery in some cases took from 18 to 50 hours. The longer recovery time could be serious if the individual re-exposed himself before full recovery occurred. In fact, after suffering an undetermined amount of acoustic assaults that cause temporary deafness, the amplified music addict, or the factory worker, may end up with noise-induced *permanent* threshold shift, or NIPTS.

Our ears, like our hearts, work 24 hours a day. The excessive acoustic stimuli to which modern man is subjected—or subjects himself—so abuses his sense of hearing that medical men speak of two phases of "ear life": the length of time the ear will serve us for hearing a wide range of sounds, and the length of time the ear will serve us for hearing speech.

In her kindness to us, unselfish Nature has made it easier for us to lose the ability to hear the upper frequencies first. This means that the first penalty of excessive noise is the loss of the ability to enjoy pastoral sounds and the full range of musical tones. High-fidelity stereo systems reproduce sounds up to 15,-000 cps or even higher. Most members of an industrialized society, by the time they reach senior citizenship, will not be able to hear 10,000 cps, let alone 15,000. The decline in hearing acuity for the male in industrialized societies begins somewhere between the ages of 25 and 30. Many millions of human beings are exposed to a lifetime of noise so intense that their frequency range drops to below 2,000 cps and they find it no longer possible to hear human speech sounds. It is believed that to understand English speech perfectly, one needs to hear all its sounds in the range from 200 to 6,000 cps. To legally qualify as having a "hearing impairment," a worker must show a substantial loss in the critical speech frequencies of 500, 1,000, and 2,000 cps.

It is tragic that excessive noise has now become a threat to man's hearing even in the pursuit of leisure. I once displayed a "skull protector" on television, and was surprised to receive a request for details from an employee of a Midwest police department. His job was to train department personnel in the use of firearms. He participated in pistol shooting and was also an avid target shooter and hunting enthusiast. Noticing difficulty in hearing women's and children's voices, he went to the Mayo Clinic. He was shocked to be told that the sound waves from shooting had damaged the cells in the nerves of his ears, that it was permanent damage, irreparable. He was told to give up shooting immediately or face the loss of hearing any normal conversation within less than a year's time.

"I also shoot skeet, trap, waterfowl, upland birds and big game. As you can imagine, this hearing deficiency takes a great part of my life away from me and my family."

He wanted the data on the skull protector, to see if his doctors would approve a limited amount of shooting if he wore one.

Perhaps adults must be held responsible for discovering the dangers of their noisy play, but children are also endangered. Children everywhere are being hurt by playing with firecrackers and toy guns, and all sorts of toys equipped with noisemaking devices.

Investigators in Oslo, Norway, proved that about 1 per cent of the 14-year-olds suffered from hearing loss that may have been caused by toys that emit impulse noises. Similar investigations in Denmark showed injuries to hearing in 3.7 per cent of boys ranging in age from 10 to 16. In 1967 the *Journal of the Acoustical Society of America* reported on the findings of foreign and American research. Investigators at the U.S. Army's Human Engineering Laboratories measured the impulse noises produced by four toy firearms, and suggested these toys pose a potential hazard to hearing. In June of 1966, *Consumer Reports* warned that the blast of a toy bazooka powered by compressed air might damage the hearing of the children using it. In 1968 the British Standards Institution took cognizance of the danger from toys, and revised its code for safety to include noise levels. Though no precise limits were set, pending additional studies, officials expected that the eventual limit may be 100 decibels at three feet from a child's ear, according to the *Manchester Guardian* of May 18, 1968.

Amplified music has developed into a threat to hearing, especially for youngsters who listen to it constantly at school, at discotheques, and at home.

It seems that every doctor or audiologist who takes a reading in a live-music discotheque is assured of a newspaper headline about the dangers found therein. Theories abound about why the threat of amplified music makes news, from the one that society is attacking the rebels where it hurts, to the other extreme that there is genuine concern for our youngsters. Whatever the reason, it must be duly noted that no comparable concern exists about the deafening situation in factories and computerized offices. Is it that adults don't matter, or that factory noise is not as exciting as the "big beat"?

It is true that even the unamplified music of the Mabaans sometimes hits 100 to 104 decibels, with final peaks of 106 and 110. However, this music (sometimes from a five-string lyre and a chorus of twenty) beats out only during the two-month spring harvest. The festival singing apparently takes place not more than three times a week, and while it lasts from one to three hours, the total exposure is hardly comparable to the year-round almost daily exposure of "civilized" youngsters.

Amplified music's impact on hearing is a touchy subject, involving the audio industry and teen-agers. Yet it cannot be ignored. Electric guitars and other amplified instruments have produced levels of from 90 to 105 decibels, with peaks of 130 decibels. These amplified sounds are especially hazardous to hearing for speech, because most of the sound energy is in the critical 500 to 3,000 cps frequency range.

This problem, like all noise problems, is international. Levels in Copenhagen nightspots frequented by young people were found to exceed 120 decibels, a definite health hazard.

Unfortunately, the relationship between temporary loss, which is the usual experience, and permanent loss is not yet understood. The head of the division of otolaryngology of the University of Florida tested his daughter and nine other teen-agers before and after a rock'n'roll session not long ago. Though he found measurable hearing loss, he did not know whether this was a temporary or a permanent loss if the levels ranged from 106 to 120 decibels.

Though more studies are needed, there seems little question but that prolonged exposure to amplified music poses a threat to hearing. For one thing, we do not know when the temporary loss blends into permanent loss, nor do we know how susceptible any given youngster is to the dangers of intense noise exposure. Another area of investigation should answer this question: if a permanent hearing loss is caused, but it is rated as only an insignificant 5-decibel loss, what happens when the victimized youngster hits middle age? The premature 5-decibel loss, added to the "normal" loss at middle age, may make the difference between a minor loss and deafness.

Annoyed neighbors may take some sadistic satisfaction in knowing that the operator of a powered lawn mower is in danger. Lawn mower noise has been measured at a range of from 92 to 105 decibels, with an average of 97. Two investigators discov-ered significant temporary hearing loss after 45 minutes of expo-sure. Aware that this can deafen the susceptible, they suggest that communities not overlook lawn mowers in their hearing-conservation programs.

Perhaps women were once wise to get out of the noise-stressed kitchen, out of their noisy homes and into the business and professional world. Except that there too—as well as coming and going—they are exposed to dangerous noise levels. But by far it is the male who pays the greater price in hearing damage. Men work in noisier occupations, operate the noisy do-it-yourself tools, hunt, commute on noisy highways, and set off the July 4th firecrackers. Civilized male hearing ages faster than that of women. But not so among the Mabaans, where men and women are equally exposed to the same environmental noise. The hearing of the Mabaan male is not significantly worse than that of the female.

There are many signs that the hearing ability of men and women of industrialized cities is declining. One of them is the shift in the baseline for the so-called loudness curves. In 1932 this baseline was zero decibels. In 1956, less than a generation later, this reference point had to be changed to plus-4 decibels. This shift is interpreted by Jansen to mean that the hearing acuity of the general population has diminished.

More and more people are finding it difficult to hear without help. The telephone company installs volume controls for the hard of hearing in hotel lobby phones; it provides optional amplified signal bells and flashing lights instead of bells. The legitimate theater uses electronic speech reinforcement where none was needed several decades ago.

When I was manager of a legitimate theater in Cincinnati I heard criticism of "dead spots" where hearing was supposed to be difficult. I invited an acoustical specialist to attend a matinee performance and advise me. During the intermission he called my attention to two women, of late middle age, sitting in front of him. He had heard perfectly. They had complained to each other that they could not catch all of the dialogue. Here was a strong indication that the problem lay with the listeners' hearing, not the theater, and not mumbling actors. Why do clergymen today need microphones for their sermons? Probably many among their congregations are suffering from partial deafness and do not know it.

Thomas Edison once predicted that as urban noise grew greater (which it inevitably would), the man of the future could eventually be born deaf.

We have long known the condition called presbycusis, age-induced hearing loss. We are now coming close to understanding occupational deafness. But the best evidence that people are having their ears hurt *outside* of work is the identification of a new category of deafness: sociocusis. Its name means hearing loss caused by a lifetime of living and playing in noisy environments.

Rosen's work in Africa is a challenge to industry's claim that there is an immutable law that adult man loses a specified amount of hearing with advancing age. One way to determine what contributes to loss of hearing with age is to measure the hearing of members of comparative societies: industrialized *vs.* primitive, quiet *vs.* noisy.

To verify the existence of sociocusis, someone would have to go through life with an ear plug in only one ear and then check his hearing to see if the protected ear retained significantly more hearing ability than the unprotected ear.

Thanks to the carelessness of a Dutch physician, there is one recorded case history in which a man did go through much of his life with one ear plugged up. Dr. A. J. Philipszoon, chief of the Ear, Nose and Throat Clinic of the University of Amsterdam, reported in 1962 that an 82-year-old man came to the clinic to try to get a hearing aid. The eardrum of his right ear was normal, but in his left ear was found a plug of cottonwool and earwax. It turned out that 32 years earlier, his family doctor, after treating the ear for an inflammation, had neglected to remove the plug of cottonwool. Dr. Philipszoon tested the hearing of both ears. The right ear showed a "normal" loss of hearing due to aging. But the hearing in the left ear was much better. The wax-encrusted plug had acted as an ear-defender for 32 years. "This case shows us 'experimentally,'" Dr. Philipszoon concluded, "that for the onset of presbycusis the noise of every day is a very important factor as suggested by Rosen."

It is estimated that perhaps ten per cent of the population may have "tin ears"—ears so sensitive that the cumulative effect of experiencing the urban noises found in transportation, on the street, and in the motorized home may lead to permanent hearing loss for the critical speech frequencies. Yet there has been no attempt to define an acceptable hearing conservation standard for the general population.

The case for recognizing noise as a health problem may be summarized as follows:

Man is being exposed to increasing amounts of a new and potent mix of stresses—chemical, physical, and psychological.

Noise, at even moderate levels, forces a systemic response from the total organism. It is not only the sense of hearing that is involved. What is also involved is what happens after the brain receives the sound signal. The brain places the body on a war footing. The repetition of these alerts is exhausting. It depletes energy levels; it can cause changes in the chemistry of the blood, in the volume of the blood circulation; it places a strain on the heart; it prevents restorative sleep and rest; it hinders convalescence; it can be a form of torture. It can so weaken the body's defense mechanisms that diseases can more readily take hold. The organism does not adapt to noise; it becomes enured and pays a price. The price of this "adaptation" is in itself a hazard to health.

The effect of noise on health may—like radiation poisoning—be something that will show no clinically significant symptoms at the time of exposure or shortly thereafter. Conclusions must not be drawn from short-term observations. Nobody, even today, knows too much about how air pollution affects people. Doctors back in the 1920's were concerned about smoking as a health hazard, but it was not until recent years that medical science was able to establish a link between smoking and health. The same lag applies to noise. Some doctors and scientists have long suspected that noise is inflicting damage, but the nature of that damage is yet to be discovered.

The most constructive medical and commonsense position is the one taken by Jansen:

Any sound or noise may *change physiological states;* and until someone will prove that these more or less repeated changes are negligible we must consider noise to have a possible detrimental influence on human health.

Noise per se may not be dangerous. But when noise becomes immoderate, as with anything else in life, it loses its innocence. It also loses its innocence when it strikes at those whose constitutions are weakened by ill health or old age. Noise may yet prove to be as deadly a threat to man as the noxious fumes about which we are presently hearing so much.

CHAPTER FOUR

The Price In Dollars

It may come as a shock to think of noise as costing money; however, it doesn't come cheap. Noise puts a multi-million dollar hole in the nation's pocket.

The most common measurement for the price of something is dollars. There have been few attempts to measure what either the individual or society is paying for excessive noise. We must face the fact that it is probably cheaper—in direct dollars—to make noise than to curb it. This is why we must recognize a price in health, and the intangibles discussed in the next chapter.

In industry alone, noise is a huge hidden extravagance. Some authorities are convinced that the potential cost of noise-induced hearing loss is greater than that of any other occupational disease. The Federal Council for Science and Technology has reported that if only ten per cent of workers eligible were to file claims, and the average award were $1,000, the total could reach $450 million.

In actuality, hearing-loss awards average $2,000. In 1962 and

1963, New York State paid $250,870 to 187 workers for hearing losses. When a drop forge plant closed down in Connecticut, the 64 men of the work force got a final settlement of $145,488, an average of $2,298 per worker. In a landmark suit against Bethlehem Steel by 323 shipyard workers, their collective claims totalled $5 million. The company settled for $250,000, plus lost time, litigation costs, and medical fees.

In the military, the tip of the iceberg of noise waste can be measured by such hard statistics as this: By 1968 the Veterans Administration was spending $65 million annually in rehabilitation programs for 90,000 veterans with service-connected hearing disorders.

Noise, authorities agree, causes an increase in errors. The Wilson Committee reported that noise above 90 decibels causes a significant rise in mistakes, particularly after the subject has been working for some time in noisy surroundings. "This effect seems to be produced even in people who are accustomed to noise," the Committee said. When they get around to studying the subject, investigators may discover that one reason for the high incidence of poor-quality manufactured products, whether automobiles or household appliances, is the noise environment in the factory.

Industry's safety programs recognize the economic cost of noise-induced accidents. Noise inhibits the prevention of accidents by obliterating or obscuring warnings or spoken signals and by masking the sounds of mechanical breakdowns. Accidents cost money in time lost, earnings lost, skills lost, medical care, the high cost of death, and the cost of training replacement personnel.

How much productivity is siphoned off by that poor night's sleep, or by that hour of sleep lost because of the 7:00 A.M. jackhammer and helicopter reveille? At the Noise Control Congress, Dr. A. Huwiler of Zurich described the effect on his patients of loss of sleep because of jet-engine warmup in the early morning:

Stress situations are caused; if they occur in the morning they represent an extremely unfavorable start to the day's work . . . . An hour of undisturbed sleep every morning, a normal physiological awakening and corresponding fitness every day for tens of thousands of people living near airports, represents an economic factor of great importance.

An analysis of our Upper Sixth Avenue petition-signers showed that office workers in the nearby highrise office buildings were disturbed, as were the staffs of the pharmacy and other specialty shops in the area.

These petitions were signed in June and July of the second year of the subway project, *after* the offending compressors had been moved underground. One can only guess at the first year's impact on accuracy, absenteeism, and productivity.

More subtle than errors, but as pervasive, are the work interruptions caused by noise. The whole hierarchy of the corporate office system suffers when noise intrudes.

The dollar cost of noise in some of its aspects is vague, hard to put one's finger on, although certainly real enough. But the loss in real estate value is plain for all to see.

In the cities, noise is a chief cause of rental turnover in new apartment buildings. Frederick P. Rose, president of a New York building management company, and a one-time delegate to the United Nations Housing Conference, says, "Of all the complaints owners hear, lack of soundproofing heads the list. And this is borne out by the experience of managing agents from coast to coast."

On Manhattan's Sixth Avenue, one apartment building had its "Apartments Available" sign out for two years because of the subway extension. It reportedly lost $7,000 a month in vacancies and unrenewed leases. Restaurants and shops in this noise-inundated neighborhood also suffered sales losses as office workers and residents detoured to quieter streets. Even banks reported a decline in off-the-street transactions.

Transportation systems—sub-surface, surface, and in the air—can be most damaging to the value of property. The Canadian government was so concerned about the decline of property values near railroad tracks that it conducted a study of the problem. The research suggested that land zoned "residential" may be depressed below its normal value unless it is 500 to 1,000 feet from the right-of-way. In Sacramento County, California, it was found that foreclosed houses on lots bordering a highway took ten months or more longer to resell than similar foreclosed houses in the same tracts away from a noisy highway.

How does one compute the cost of highway noise, noise so disturbing to sleep that in 1961 eight communities along the New York section of the New England Thruway organized the Thruway Noise Abatement Committee? The local officials felt it was more than worth the $15,000 for noise tests and the four years of time spent in politicking to get New York State to enact the first decibel limit for motor vehicles. Their motivation was the protection of homes near highways, homes the value of which could be as readily depreciated as once were homes near railroad tracks.

The most audible cries of anguish come from people unfortunate enough to own property near airports. Not too many years ago, a Congressional hearing received this list of litigation due to aircraft noise:

Atlanta—73 suits pending for a total of $5 million;

Memphis—20 suits pending, aggregating $2 million;

New York—A suit filed by 808 plaintiffs against 39 airlines and the Port of New York Authority, totaling $1 million;

Seattle—200 suits pending, totaling $1 million;

Los Angeles—38 claims, totaling $1 million.

Other claims in Ontario and San Francisco, California; Dallas; Denver; Houston; Jackson; Oklahoma City; Phoenix; Omaha; Portland, Oregon; San Antonio; Spokane, and Tampa;

Suits threatened in Dayton and Nashville.

This sort of thing goes on all over. In Paris, ten town councils filed suits against Air France and Pan American Airways for noise nuisance, asking damages in the millions, covering costs of soundproofing buildings near Orly Airport. In Norway, 32 homeowners sued the Ministry of Defense and Communications and won 185,000 kroner, about $26,300, for discomfort and property devaluation caused by jet noise.

Cities pay in the deterioration of their neighborhoods. Acoustician Lew Goodfriend hit where it hurts when he observed that the geographically extensive impact of aviation and highway noise affects the entire social and economic structure of the city. "This could be serious if it results in middle and upper class families abandoning neighborhoods, quietly and without fanfare, leaving them to the next lower economic level for whom the neighborhood, noisy or not, is a step upward."

This deterioration is happening. In Miami, it is reported that because of jet runways built near a housing development, people who could afford to moved away in spite of tax benefits. Whereas earlier the residents of that development represented a median income group of $15,000 to $20,000 a year, in six years the income range dropped to between $7,000 and $8,000.

When supersonic aircraft climb into the wild blue yonder, they send back calling cards in the form of sonic booms. It is reported that in 1965, the Air Force received 3,000 formal complaints, and paid out some $250,000 in reparations. An Interior Department study makes the "conservative estimate [that] the expected continuing annual cost of the repair of damages to houses and other structures, not counting the cost of processing claims or inspection of damages, is at least $35 million, and possibly more than $80 million per year."

Expensive, isn't it, this noise business?

How do we begin to estimate the loss in dollars from the loss of the right to be heard? What is the dollar value of an idea lost? How do we tot up the loss in creativity? Creative people are finding it increasingly difficult to function in our noisy cities. A playwright told me, "My mind's eye has my characters on stage. I'm working out a problem. Suddenly a siren knifes by. The characters leave the stage. It takes me quite a while to get them back on again. I find the city stimulating, but the noise inhibits my output."

Many writers and other creative people must leave the city to finish an assignment, and the cost is paid not only by the individual, but by the city that is left behind. Many large corporations —and the middle class—have been leaving cities such as New York, fleeing to the "quieter" suburbs. The cities are in bad enough economic shape already, without being further drained by the tyranny of noise.

Noise-ridden city hotels might enjoy a higher occupancy rate if they could provide a quiet night's sleep. Many exurbanites are starting to write off even the occasional weekend on the town, as did one insurance executive and his wife:

"Alice and I," he said, "moved to the suburbs to get away from the racket. But we couldn't live without coming back to the city to do the town, see some plays, eat at a nice restaurant, and stay overnight at a hotel. But we found that the longer we lived in the suburbs, the less we could stand the noise of the city at night. Now we still come in occasionally, but just for a few hours. We go home for a good night's rest."

Someone soon will write his Ph.D. dissertation on the cost to society of soundproofing structures to keep out noises from the street and from the skies. Whether it is 2 per cent or 5 per cent or 10 per cent extra, to the cost of noise must be added the cost of sound-conditioning homes, offices, theaters, and motels. Because National Airport in Washington now permits jets, an additional $5 million has to be spent on soundproofing the new Kennedy Cultural Center. Some inkling of the cost of soundproofing structures near airports is the multi-million dollar lawsuit of the Los Angeles City Unified School District against the Department of Airports, a sum based on the estimated cost of soundproofing the several schools where classroom instruction is interrupted by jet noise.

One builder reported that a sandwich wall of acoustical insulation between its staggered studs may cost $200 more for 1,650 square feet of house. Full carpeting may add another $500. Sound-trapped air conditioning systems are necessary because windows must be kept closed.

One Englishman living near Heathrow Airport double-glazed four windows and fitted three of them with sound-trapped ventilating units developed by the British government. It cost him £258— £120 for the window treatment, £120 for the ventilating units, and 18 for fitting them. The government reimbursed him the sum of £100.

The most costly sound insulation is required by homes near airports. Roofs may have to be insulated, as well as windows. According to one Federal study, it could cost from $260 to $4,500 to sound-insulate a detached house made of light exteriors, and from $260 to $3,400 to sound-insulate a house with heavy exterior walls. Ventilation improvements would be additional.

Premiums for noise abatement are a forced price for survival. Even though it would be dollar-cheaper, communities would not discontinue requiring the pasteurization of milk. We are being forced into the "pasteurization" of unwanted sound along with procedures as routine as those for building safety, fire prevention, and the other protective steps adopted by modern man to make his environment compatible with his needs.

Is it less expensive to develop a quieter form of airplane propulsion, or to insulate thousands of homes near airports? What of the dollar and social costs of relocation for thousands of residents who can't afford to insulate?

In 1965, after filling my umpteenth prescription for sedatives and buying a new wax-type earplug, I jokingly told my pharmacist that someday drugstores would be barometers of noise assault. Today investigators of the noise problem are seriously considering adopting the sales of earplugs in local drugstores as a guide to the degree of noise stress in non-occupational environments. An informal survey of drugstores near construction sites indicates that as the jackhammers move in, the sales of earplugs and aspirins go up. A good portion of the noise-cost index must be in the $400 million spent annually on headache remedies. Workers are buying incredible quantities of drugs to keep them awake and to put them to sleep. The illegal acquisition and use of stimulants and depressants in industry, especially among production-line workers, is alleged to be so common, according to an article in *The New York Times* Sunday Magazine, "that to arrest everybody who sold or used them would mean that some plants would have to hire whole new shifts of employees." If for a given year only one million noise-stressed people took tranquilizers for a conservative 20 weeks at an average cost of $3 a week, this could come to $60 million a year. If more than one million people average more than 20 weeks of tranquilizers, and also take aspirins and sleeping pills, and pep pills to overcome fatigue from noise and poor sleep . . . .

Since noise has been shown to be one cause of hearing loss, some of the money spent on hearing aids must be charged to noise. It has been estimated that between 10 and 15 million Americans need hearing aids for their various types of hearing loss. The Hearing Aid Industry Conference estimates that more than a million and a half Americans do wear hearing aids. The World Health Organization reports that the actual hearing-aid rate in urban areas is estimated to be around 6.8 per 1,000 population, rising from 1.3 per 1,000 persons under 45 years of age to 72.6 per 1,000 persons for those aged 75 and over.

Hearing aids sell for from as little as $75 to as much as $500 for a binaural (two-ear) set. It is impossible to compute what share of this market can be credited to noise, but if six to sixteen million American workers are already deafened, and city noise damages hearing, noise is a good salesman.

Though nothing is known about how many people enter hospitals because of noise-induced illness, the Public Health Service has something to say about the cost of noise once the patient is hospitalized. A PHS report justified expenditures for noise control by informing hospital planners that "added days of hospital care, extended convalescence, or incomplete recovery may result from patient's insufficient bed rest. Moreover, the monetary loss to the community and to the individual in terms of lost working days from long hospitalization is a further reason for providing quieter hospital conditions." In other words, expensive hospital stays may be prolonged by noise.

Noise drives one to escape as much as possible. Few of us think of the cost of escape from noise. To economist Sylvia Porter, that house in the country is no longer a luxury for city man, but necessary for his survival. *Publishers Weekly* describes the conscientious editor as one who has "probably sunk his meager present and future earnings into a quiet little place in the country, where he can work in peace."

Those who cannot afford the outlay for that country house must pay heavily for periodic escapes. This price goes up as the nearby havens of quiet disappear and only distance offers the hope of fewer decibels. "Refugees from noise," writes Homer Bigart in *The New York Times*, "now have somewhere to go." That "somewhere" is the hotels Laurance Rockefeller has developed in the West Indies and Hawaii, resorts that "woo peace, privacy, and tranquility. None is readily accessible to a city. The poor man is left with ear plugs."

For those who cannot afford the actual sounds of nature, there are the synthetic "white noise" devices. At a cost of $11.50 you can listen to a recording of something that is supposed to lull like the "swooshing pine-woods winds." For $69.95 you will get, it is claimed, the magic sound of the sea.

Thousands, perhaps millions of noise victims complain, and many protest to local officialdom. We cannot begin to estimate the cost in energy expended organizing, writing Letters to the Editor, badgering City Hall, petitioning, suing, picketing, and pursuing the noisemaker. This all takes time, and time is money.

City Hall and the noisemaker have found it costs money to reply, to placate. Contractors sometimes assign someone to cope with the protests; the FAA operates a number of local noise abatement offices; politicians must take time out to help constituents. It would have been less costly to install quality mufflers and sound barriers around the compressors and quiet the jackhammers, than to spend time and man-hours to contain the USANAA.

As we continue probing the new concept of environmental quality we will discover that the total cost of excessive noise is something society cannot afford.

CHAPTER FIVE

The Price In Environmental Quality

Certain things creep up on man without his noticing them. Old age, deafness, the loss of his human rights, and the loss of the quality of life. If the war in Viet Nam stopped tomorrow, if enough housing was built, enough schools, if poverty and discrimination were ended—a noisy technology would still deny us the right to rest, the right to sleep, the right to be let alone. "Technology," says Wilbur H. Ferry, "touches the person and the common life more intimately and often than does any government. Technology's scope places in the hands of its administrators gigantic capabilities for arbitrary power."

Suddenly we see that, impersonal and blind, noise hits the sick and the well, the old and the young, the student and the vacationer, the hospital patient and the doctor, the factory worker and the farmer, the judge and the prisoner. Indeed, we are all prisoners of noise. A political dictator could not have more impact on how one lives than the operators of jets and jackhammers. Democracy gives man the right to vote, but not the right to sleep; the right to dissent, but not the right to minimize the noises of social utility; the right to go to school, but not the right to be able to hear the teacher. Under the guise of waging a necessary, therefore holy, war for progress, technology strips man of his dignity, his right to meditate and work creatively, his means of maintaining the well-being of his soul.

Morale is an intangible asset. What happens to the human spirit? When New York's new Metropolitan Transportation Authority announced plans for a Second Avenue Subway, the most typical attitude was that expressed by a middle-aged veteran of city life. Throwing up his hands in despair, he cried out, "I accept it. I live in New York, and I accept what happens."

But some New Yorkers have fought. They have picketed, petitioned, testified at hearings, tried the courts. All to no avail. The public is ignored into submission. The individual "may roar and yelp a bit," says Ferry, "and declare there ought to be a law. Then he subsides to a mutter and ultimately silence, which is precisely what the noisemakers count on."

Jean-Paul Sartre, in his play *No Exit,* described Hell as never to be let alone. The growing noise intrusion is creating this type of hell right here on earth. Man has lost the right to be let alone. He must respond to the distractions of noises that are not even meant for his ears. Unable to shut them out, he is constantly at the mercy of the acoustic stimuli generated by others.

To Norman Cousins, "Silence is not nothingness or the absence of sound. It is a prime condition for human serenity and the natural environment of contemplation. A life without regular periods of silence is a life without essential nourishment for both the spirit and the functioning intelligence. Silence offers the vital element of privacy, without which an individual becomes something less than himself . . . . We live at a time when thought alone represents the difference between sanity and total madness. One of the prime requirements of such thought is privacy and a little silence, at least now and then."

Cousins was addressing himself to the readers of an intellectual magazine in 1962. Five years later, in 1967, *Life* Magazine, addressing itself to a much broader readership, showed the same concern for the destruction of solitude by noise. "The escalating noise problem," it editorialized, "may require the widespread rediscovery of the personal value of silence. Most religions throughout human history have insisted that man needs regular intervals of silence for spiritual health."

It erodes one's belief in human decency to observe what society does even to the sick.

The telephone rang one sunny day in the CQC office. It was a member of our Board of Directors, the late Dr. William Vogt. His wife, I knew, was a cancer patient at Columbia Presbyterian Medical Center, one of the leading hospitals in the United States.

"My wife has been in a coma for two weeks; she is dying. There is a construction project outside her hospital room. The noise is dreadful. Ask someone to do something. Call the City!"

Call the City—! He had forgotten that construction noise is the legal price of progress and that city noise must be endured in payment for the amenities of a civilized society.

But are the "amenities" of civilization, whatever those may be, worth the price in degradation? Our ancestors banded together to build walls to keep out marauders and Indian arrows. We moderns are less successful with sound energy.

The failure of home design to insulate the noisy activities of the children is especially distracting to parents who find it difficult to tune out their multiple sounds. The normal stresses of family life are aggravated by this noise. Husbands made irascible by their daily work, plus commuting noise, find it difficult to step into a noisy home with equanimity. Jansen's studies of German steel workers suggest that men who work in noisy jobs display a higher incidence of domestic difficulties than those who work in quieter jobs. From farmers riding noisy tractors to business-

men who end a day in a noisy office in a rattling bar car that far from tranquilizes the day's tensions, no one is immune.

Housewives are forced to bear the brunt of society's legalization of daytime open-air noises. A reader writes to *Good Housekeeping* Magazine: "I believe the constant din from our busy streets is literally making me ill. My husband says that's nonsense—that noise may make me deaf, but can't make me sick. Which of us is right?" The magazine answered: "You may well be."

If noise isn't making her sick, it may be undermining her marriage.

In contemporary homes, husband and wife are denied privacy for the intimacies of marriage. Dr. Haim G. Ginott, author of *Between Parent and Child*, describes our homes as "antisex." "Few modern houses or apartments," he writes, "have deliberate safeguards for sexual privacy . . . . It is a sad comment on our civilization that the sounds of legitimate love must be so low."

In today's architecture, no allowance is made for keeping outsiders from sharing the bedroom experience with the participants. Thin walls bring neighbors into the bedroom to cheer or jeer, as in the story of the man whose wife played hard to get. When she finally verbalized her assent, cries of "Congratulations, Hugo!" rang out, it is said, from the next *two* apartments.

Noise is the most personal and psychologically intimate of all the forms of pollution. It allows impersonal machines and other human beings to get unbearably close.

Writers of marriage manuals are starting to recognize the environmental imperatives. The authors of *Sexual Adventure in Marriage* offer advice on how "to circumvent noise, to create interludes of privacy for two that can refresh the senses and spirit." One suggestion for quiet surroundings for lovemaking: underwater. In scuba equipment?

Someday, noise is likely to be implicated as a factor in frigidity. Sudden noises will be discovered to short-circuit the sexual response by shunting it to a secondary track while the body goes on to a state of alert. Couples experiencing difficulty in conceiving will be advised to wear earmuffs, or take to the water in snorkels.

Modern man no less than his primitive ancestors must depend upon his ears to warn him of danger. In 1930, New York City's Noise Commission reported that "There are many places where a tiger from Siberia or Bengal could roar or snarl without attracting the auditory attention of the passersby." In 1968, human tigers could murder in the city jungle and not be heard. On January 18 of that year, a middle-aged jeweler, held up in his shop in the heart of Times Square, was shot, not once, not twice, but four times without any of the scores of pedestrians hearing a sound. The shots were drowned out by the noise of compressed air hammers and other equipment at construction sites nearby. The two holdup men escaped.

When a 13-year-old New Jersey girl was found beaten and strangled to death 75 feet from the back door of a neighbor's home, the neighbor's son told reporters: "My father heard nothing. None of us heard anything. We had the air conditioning running all night." A quality environment should, at the very least, have noise levels low enough to permit shots and screams to be heard.

When you hear that helicopter noise is not different from any other city noise, think of the two people who were killed when Senator Robert Kennedy's funeral train was passing through Elizabeth, New Jersey—killed because the noise from the low-flying Secret Service and news media helicopters masked out the warning horn blasts of the approaching train that hit them.

Someday, highway noise will be discovered to be a significant cause of traffic accidents.

Churches are no more a sanctuary from noise assault than the secular environment. Noise intrusion has no respect even for death. Mourners find that the sanctity of the graveside funeral service is violated by construction noise and lawn mowers.

The minister of one local church near a USAF base in England arranged for a "hot line" between the base and his church: a phonecall silences the jets for weddings, funerals, and other special services. Churches near commercial airports are not as fortunate. They must either build soundproofed structures or endure interrupted services. In ruling against the Town of Hempstead's attempt to control jet noise over its land area, the courts acknowledged that church services were interrupted, but accepted this as the price of progress.

Perhaps the most dramatic example of how commerce and technology are defiling our environment is provided by the advent of the supersonic transport, the needle-nosed SST.

Fear of what the SST will do to man and his environment is being increasingly voiced by scientists and government officials alike. Don Dwiggins, for many years the aerospace editor of the Los Angeles *Mirror News*, in 1968 wrote a book, *The SST: Here It Comes, Ready Or Not.* At the end of this carefully documented work, he told his readers that he had discovered the villain of his story to be "the SST itself."

Why all the concern about this new type of plane, while the prosaic noises of surface transportation and even the subsonic jets have yet to arouse the public—or government—to effective action?

The reason is an eerie phenomenon spelled b-o-o-m, sonic boom—a physical reaction to the rupturing of the sound barrier as an airplane travels faster than sound. This boom is not something that happens only once, when the plane breaks the sound barrier. The sonic boom, somewhat like the wake of a ship, is a "sonic carpet" that accompanies the plane as long as it flies supersonically. As described by Dr. Bo Lundberg, a Swedish aviation authority, the conical pressure wave becomes strong and hits the ground in every spot within a "boom carpet" which stretches miles wide continuously along the entire flight path. The typical boom is a shock wave, caused by the air compressed by supersonic flight. The wave of compressed air exerts physical pressure against whatever stands in its path.

We do not as yet know what the commercial sonic boom will be like. But we already know what booms from smaller supersonic planes will be like. We have a Canadian military pilot to thank for giving us some inkling of what the boom can do to structures. Flying an F-104 supersonic jet fighter, he accidentally flew supersonically at an altitude of 500 feet. Nothing much might have happened had he been flying over the desert, but he was flying over the temporary control tower and the terminal building of the almost-completed Ottawa airport.

Don Dwiggins, in his book on the SST, summarized what happened to the structures:

> With a mighty concussion the control tower literally exploded, showering glass in all directions. The terminal roof was ripped open and aluminum flashing strips were thrown across the access road. A curtain wall over the ticket lobby was distorted. Large glass panes in the terminal were smashed. Four doorways suffered severe damage. Exterior stucco broke away, and crashed to the ground.
>
> Throughout the new building the ceiling was blown apart, the recessed fluorescent fixtures left skewed, pushed up, or left hanging down, as if wrenched and tortured by a severe earthquake.

It cost the government of Ottawa $300,000 to repair the damage. The flight pattern, was, of course, against the rules.

It may be argued that this was an accident, but even in normal operation the sonic boom has a destructive effect on natural and man-made structures. In 1968, reports of damage to cliff dwellings in the National Parks System prompted the then-Secretary of the Interior Stewart Udall to initiate his own study of the boom. Park engineers reported damage in Canyon de Chelly National Monument in northeastern Arizona and to geological formations in Bryce National Park in Utah, and potential damage to Mesa Verde National Park in Colorado. An estimated 80 tons of overhanging cliff fell on a cliff dwelling in Canyon de Muerto.

The Interior Department's 1968 sonic boom report (Udall) leaves little room for complacency. The scientists who wrote the report observed that unlike subsonic jets, which impact an area basically within a radius of 12 to 15 miles of airports, the SST, even if flown at high altitudes, creates new noise corridors on the ground tens of miles wide along its flight path so that ". . . potentially no land area would be free from some noise intrusion."

Dr. Lundberg was the first to warn the world about the meaning of the sonic boom. He believes that "in the supersonic age it will be inadvisable to take a siesta, or leave a child in a pram, on a balcony, or beside a garden wall." Thanks to military supersonic flight, at least one French family didn't have to wait for the supersonic age of commercial aviation. Here is the havoc as described by Walter Sullivan, Science editor of *The New York Times:* "Last week a French farm family, with eight neighbors and hired hands helping in the harvest, gathered for the noon meal in a farmhouse near the village of Mauran in Brittany. Suddenly, according to accounts from France, a sound like a thunderclap was heard. Timbers shook loose and eight tons of barley stored in a loft fell on those eating, killing three and injuring one seriously. Apparently it was the first time that a sonic boom had been blamed for fatal injuries."

Apparently these Bretons didn't know enough to adapt to one of the new "minor stresses" of modern living.

Understandably, then, there is a raging controversy over whether or not the SST should be permitted to fly at supersonic speeds over land. If such flights are permitted, according to the Udall study, sometime after 1975 between 20 million and 40 million Americans would be boomed five to fifty times a day under a path 12½ miles to either side of the flight paths. An additional 35 million to 65 million people within a path 12½ to

25 miles to either side of the flight path would be subjected to from one to fifty booms per day of somewhat lower intensity, and 13 million to 25 million more would experience one to four high-intensity booms. In short, up to 130 million Americans a day would be exposed daily to the boom.

According to the Interior Department study, here is how people react to sonic booms:

" . . . There is considerable initial adaptation following several months of exposure, but even after several years of experiencing booms, most people find the booms objectionable or worse. Extensive research at Edwards Air Force Base, Oklahoma City, and in France, shows that even after some years of continued exposure to sonic booms, 30 per cent of the people exposed to booms at levels anticipated for the SST would find the booms to be 'intolerable' or 'unacceptable' and an additional 50 per cent would find them 'objectionable.'

"Persons experiencing sonic booms are startled and diverted or, if asleep, may be awakened in the same manner as those who hear an unexpected loud thunderclap or a large explosion. These effects may be accompanied by increased pulse rate and other minor and transient physiological changes, but they are not believed to be harmful in themselves, nor to endanger hearing."

It should be noted that in the body of this study it is admitted that "No tests on experimental animals or on human beings have been conducted over a sufficiently long period of time to detect possible chronic effects, or effects of long-repeated exposures to sonic booms. . . . Tests conducted to date have not explored fully many of the situations in which sonic boom annoyance might be amplified. How extensive, for example, would be the interruption of cultural and artistic activities in which quiet and concentration are important? What is likely to be the impact upon infants, sleeping children, hospitalized persons or other individuals whose immediate well-being requires uninterrupted sleep or freedom from excessive noise? Studies to date have not considered these kinds of situations."

In his documented source book on the SST and the sonic boom, William A. Shurcliff, Ph.D., Director of the Citizens League Against the Sonic Boom, provides further information on why the sonic boom is a new noise, to be taken seriously:

"The boom is annoying because it is so loud, so sudden, and occurs with no warning whatsoever. It sounds much like the 'bang' produced by a moderate-size explosion a block away. Because it strikes with no warning (and no visible explanation), the boom evokes man's primitive startle reaction. . . . The surgeon making a delicate incision will jump too."

This source book further describes the adverse effect of noise on sleep. During the Oklahoma City sonic boom tests (sponsored by NASA and the FAA), "18 per cent of the persons polled complained of sleep-interference by the boom—even though the booms did not start each day until 7:00 A.M., and even though the average overpressure of the booms was only 60 per cent of the overpressure expected of [commercial] SSTs' booms. Many persons used the 7:00 A.M. boom as an 'alarm clock'—and did not 'get used to it.' "

Hidden in the government reports of sonic boom tests is the word "average." The reference is to the average boom pressure. The incidents reported above were presumably caused by the *average* type of sonic boom. But Dr. Lundberg has called attention to the "superbang," a sonic boom that exceeds the average pressure by a multiple of two or more. In the tests conducted at Oklahoma City, Lundberg observed that "at every point within the whole carpet, one boom strike in a thousand is twice as strong or more than the average on the track." Many factors contribute to the formation of a superbang: atmospheric conditions such as temperature changes, winds, local turbulence, cloud formations, flight operations such as turns and accelerations. It does not look as if local or even Federal laws will stop these.

Though only one boom in 10,000 is likely to be a superbang, they will be frequent occurrences because of the millions of people and structures that will be struck in the boom carpet. Lundberg believes that conservatively speaking, 10 million people could be exposed to superbooms in the boom carpet of the New York-to-Los Angeles run. He further believes that this enormous mass of severe boom strikes will inevitably result in many serious accidents, for example by falling glass, or even deaths, by heart failure.

If overland flights are banned and supersonic speed permitted only over water, how easy will it be for commercial fishermen, and steamship passengers and crew, to settle their claims for sonic boom damage?

How effective will protest be, even if 50 million are boomed? Only a small minority will know how to or be prompted to protest. Also, it will be much simpler to repatch the plaster than to go through the red tape of processing a complaint against the government.

Replying to those who say we must accept the sonic boom as another noise stress, Lundberg says it is illogical and cynical to ask us to accept the sonic boom just because we suffer from jet, traffic, and other noises. "The very fact that local noise is unavoidable these days, makes it, of course, all the more important that the countryside and quiet suburbs are kept undisturbed. Only then will it remain possible for those who are noise ridden during part of the day to recover in the evenings and nights and during weekends, holidays, and sickness."

Meanwhile the international race to introduce the SST continues.

Less dramatic than the sonic boom, but no less disturbing, is the effect of noise on personal communication. Very rarely these days can we hear the sound of the human voice as a solo. Even in the theater we must listen to the actors' voices plus the sounds of the ventilating or air conditioning system.

Mechanical noises also pollute the atmosphere of concerts, outdoors as well as indoors. Noise won over music when the

New York City Parks Department opened its outdoor stage at Damrosch Park. The music critic of *The New York Times* accepted seven jets, one four-engine prop plane, and one helicopter, all in the first fifteen minutes of the concert, as "par for an outdoor concert in the city." But he could not accept the concerto for air conditioning system which played the entire concert from the bowels of the adjacent Metropolitan Opera House, a concerto which "roars like a sizeable waterfall and never stops." Not even the amplifying system could overcome these external noises.

Kindergarten children attending a school near New York's Central Park were taken for a walk and then asked to list the outdoor sounds they had heard. The majority of the sounds they named were noises, mostly from transportation. There were few mentions of quiet sounds like birds and human voices. Transportation noises are becoming more "natural" to these youngsters than the sounds of nature.

Will society have to develop special soundproofed "museums" where people can go to hear the pure sounds of music, the spoken word, and nature?

To fully enjoy music and hear it as the composer intended, it is essential to hear the high frequencies. It is true, observes Yeshiva University music professor Dr. Edward Levy, that the fundamental tone is below 2,000 cps, but, if the ear loses its potential acuity, it loses the ability to distinguish timbre, or tone color. Berlioz, Brahms, Debussy, Berg, and many others carefully took advantage of the differences in timbre among various instruments. As for contemporary composers and their new electronic material, most of it is in the higher frequencies. Those with hearing loss, Dr. Levy believes, will lose contact with this new music. Of course, one may not choose ever to listen to it all, but it's nice to know one could.

The partial loss of hearing is somewhat analogous to faulty vision. Sounds are blurred, sounds are dimmed, and some sounds are not heard at all.

The transition from mild hearing loss, if we can call the loss of full-frequency hearing mild, to total deafness is like going from a sentence of probation to a lifetime sentence of solitary confinement. One hearing specialist describes the gradual loss of hearing thusly: "The humming, buzzing, rattling sounds of everyday life slip away. Friends' and relatives' diction becomes increasingly sloppy." The person who becomes deaf or "hard of hearing" lives in a world of subdued sound, or even silence. He has lost his primary means of communication and tends to withdraw from the world and live within himself, a comparative recluse.

Deafness, it is said, is more of an isolation from humankind than blindness. Deaf people, it is said, seldom smile. Unverified reports claim a greater tendency to suicide among those who become deaf than among those who go blind. Helen Keller has been quoted as saying that the world's "normal" people have never been roused to mass sympathy for the affliction. "It causes no fever, no crutches, no seeing-eye dog, not even a sneeze," she told interviewer Phyllis Battelle.

Earlier Miss Keller had written: "Deafness, like poverty, stunts and deadens its victims."

Even total deafness offers no escape from traffic and aviation noise, which have much of their energy in the lower frequencies. City planner Clifford R. Bragdon has reported that a totally deaf man living near Philadelphia's airport conveyed to him that he was constantly awakened by vibrations from low-flying aircraft.

Hearing aids are no panacea. For one thing, they are not always helpful for deafness attributable to noise. For another, their use can exaggerate the impact of sudden noises.

From an article in *Today's Health* comes this information: "Another problem of hearing aid users: sudden loud sounds. The roar of a jet, the scream of a police siren—these can be extremely painful." The article indicates one possible solution, an automatic gain control that cuts out when the sudden sound signal is intense, and comes on again when the noise diminishes.

Note that the hearing aid user is twice a victim—when he suffers his hearing loss, and when he discovers that the device he must use to compensate for that loss in itself adds to his discomfort and alienation from his fellow man.

For the deaf aged, aural separation from the world of wanted sounds adds to loneliness, itself one of the most painful afflictions of old age. Thus in what should be their golden years, our senior citizens must lose their ability to hear the comforting sounds of their loved ones, and must be cut off from the warming, stimulating sounds of music, nature, and so forth. I don't know why I say "our senior citizens," as if most of us were not destined to become senior citizens.

The brutalization of our society by noise is revealed by what we are doing to our children, exposing them to such excessive noise in their formative years that they tune out in self-defense and have to be educated to listen to verbal communication. The Mabaan children are taught to listen for self-protection. Educators have told me it is a commonplace in a city like New York that new pupils coming from low-income areas also have to be trained to listen. At home, amid probably many brothers and sisters demanding attention against the external noises of raucous street activities and heavy traffic, the children have heard speech chiefly as grunts, and had to pick even those out from among many other generalized human sounds. Apparently, in the act of screening out the destructive sounds of their environment, they have lost the art of focussing on speech sounds.

Pre-talking-age children who constantly hear noise-masked speech do not receive the full auditory value of the speech sounds in their surroundings. Consonants and vocal nuances are masked, filtered out, and the child learns an imperfect vocal pattern.

Tune-outs, especially among the underprivileged, growing up

in noisy environments, may later become drop-outs.

But noise is becoming an economic equalizer, and all children are beginning to suffer. Well-to-do mothers seek apartments that face away from traffic, and they man the picket lines to oppose heliports and jetports.

As if to assure ourselves that our children will be prepared for tomorrow's noise-saturated world, we allow excessive noise to accompany them during their school hours. Most schools seem designed to be reverberation boxes. Hard floors and ceilings amplify the normal sounds of school activities. The students are sitting ducks for decibels. This is what one small-town Texas high school environment sounded like to a college professor of Health and Physical Education:

"In a single wing of the building, a half dozen classrooms are hammered with afternoon noises—Vocational Education classes. The efficiency and effectiveness of the lecture classes drop and the students strain to hear. Fatigue and irritability of students and teachers is great."

What happens to the quality of education when teachers are exposed to fatigue and irritation from noise? "I have found the noise to be an abomination," wrote one private-school teacher. "In the classroom, concentration is difficult and I have to raise my voice to be heard. I must choose between opening the window and not being heard or leaving the window closed and subjecting my pupils to stuffiness and sleepiness. After classes there is no relief. I live here at the school and cannot escape the noise [of construction going on in the vicinity] to relax after a trying day of teaching. Over a period of time, this has seriously interfered with my work, as my enthusiasm and effectiveness in the classroom is directly dependent upon complete relaxation during free hours."

Too many schools have been built near jetports, or vice versa, and aviation noise is lessening the efficiency of the educational process. So frequent are interrruptions from aviation, they are now clocked and inserted into the *Congressional Record*. The

Superintendent of Schools of Inglewood, California, told a Congressional subcommittee:

"As for our instructional program, we must point out that oral communication becomes impossible each time a jet aircraft passes near our schools. This means that approximately 165 teachers and 4,000 students must stop all class discussion until the aircraft has progressed beyond the schools. The result of such disruption goes beyond the actual time involved in the passage of the aircraft and each class must again have its attention focussed on what was being done before the interruption. ... Our teachers tell us that as the number of jet planes increases they find classroom instruction increasingly difficult and it is their feeling that considerable loss in the educational program results."

Some school architects are now eliminating windows or planning underground classrooms.

Handicapped children suffer most. The impact of sudden noises on children with epilepsy and other diseases forces parents to seek forms of escape. One mother wrote me to inquire after a source for the acoustic earmuffs she had seen me demonstrate on television. "My son is extremely sensitive to loud noises, both sharp and sudden. . . . There are many activities he would like to participate in—but due to this problem he cannot do so at this time. He seems to tolerate moderate noises but anything above a normal high or sharp tone disturbs him. He is a cerebral palsy boy with tension, and has a severe problem with loud and sharp noises."

By giving moral and legal sanction to noisemaking, we have made outcasts of those who suffer from noise. They are made to be ashamed of their suffering, as if it indicated some flaw in their character, a desire to stop civilization's progress. They feel constrained not to convey to their family or friends how they feel. Many choose to suffer silently, rather than chance ridicule.

Among the hundreds of letters CQC received after my appearance on the Johnny Carson *Tonight* Show was one from an elderly woman who found relief in writing to an organization that understood what she was going through. All her life, she wrote, she not only suffered from noise, but had to hold back her complaints.

CQC's first office was a sublet in the Theatre Guild building. A public relations man wandered into the place one day by accident. Instead of excusing himself and departing, his eyes fastened on our name plate. Cool and poised, this Madison Avenue huckster started asking questions about our operation. Suddenly he plunged from his poised demeanor into an agonizing description of his own noise problem.

"They've just opened up the second bar within earshot of my apartment. These two spots have become the 'in' spots with the sports car crowd. I can't sleep. And now the building across the street has just installed a giant air conditioning unit on the roof opposite my window. That constant roaring is driving me bugs —" And then he stopped as suddenly as he had started, visibly embarrassed. "My God, I'm not a complainer. I didn't mean to complain. I must sound like a kook."

Torture is defined as something that causes agony or pain, suffering, annoyance. These are the very terms the public and our social commentators use to describe what noise is doing to us.

Noise exposure and its effects are not unlike the non-violent techniques used to torture captives since time immemorial. Dr. Zhivko D. Angelusheff, a staff member of the Speech and Hearing Center of New York's City Hospital, cites a third-century B.C. Chinese suggestion that instead of hanging criminals, "flutes, drums, and chimes or bells should be sounded without letup, until they drop dead, because this is the most agonizing death man could ever think of. . . . Ring, ring the bells without interruption until the criminals first turn insane then die."

As man advanced up the rungs of the ladder of civilization he improved his methods of applying noise torture, and expanded their practice. The Nazis used the whine of Stuka dive bombers to terrorize civilian populations; when all else failed, they broke the will of concentration camp prisoners with an unbearable noise.

Dictatorships seem not to be able to forego noise torture. A young Greek told a news conference that he had seen a man accused of being a Communist, but who maintained his innocence, tortured for three months by excessive pressure on his extremities, and by intolerable reverberations from a bell outside his cell. The Russian Communists in turn expose their political prisoners to a novel form of modern noise torture, nothing as primitive as beating bells, or gongs. They simply place them in a noisy factory in a Siberian labor camp.

The Russian writer Anatoly T. Marchenko, himself a prisoner, told *The New York Times* what happened when another writer, Yuli M. Daniel, was transferred to a machine shop: "The noise in the machine shop was loud enough to split the head of even the least sensitive of men. Daniel suffered from ear trouble, and the prison staff knew this. The result was that Daniel, who was only slightly hard of hearing when he came into the camp, is now almost deaf."

In the United States and all of the industrialized countries of the world we expose men to the same conditions as the price of earning a living. What kind of a society is it that allows men to work under conditions which in a Soviet prison camp are punishment?

The classical use of torture was for a purpose: to demoralize, to force a confession. The horror of today's torture by noise is that it is inflicted on a hapless civilian population without purpose. The consumer is not the enemy of commerce and industry; why is he treated as such?

Constant, nagging noise brings out the worst in man. One of the reasons John Connell formed the British Noise Abatement Society was his discovery of "the deep widespread feelings of hatred generated in the minds of captive audiences forced to listen." Noise is seized upon as a rationale for deep-rooted prejudice, and all too frequently complaints of neighbor noise describe the offending party by ethnic background, as in: "I live in a city project, next door to nine Puerto Ricans, seven teen-agers. . . a loud juke-box is played all day and most of the night. There is nothing but a drunken cabaret of gaiety going on all day and most of the night. . . . The architects who designed these projects ought to be forced to live in them."

Mayor Lindsay failed to understand the influence of noise on social relationships when he ordered an investigation of hippie riots in Tompkins Square Park. He wanted a report on why a riot should erupt out of a group engaged in what he saw as "noisy but generally harmless activity." The bongos and Buddhist love chants were not deemed a harmless activity by the old-timers living in the area. Two youths and eleven policemen were injured and 38 persons were arrested because, among other things, pre-existing tensions between the resident Puerto Ricans and Slavs were aggravated by an alien noise. One minister described the differing social and cultural values as creating a "powder keg." An intellectual living in the area told a reporter that the Poles, Czechs, Ruthenians, and Ukranians are a stolid type who go in for law and order in a big way, and hate the disorder of the hippies and their noise.

Fury is also generated by the legalized nuisances of society. One woman who was experiencing nighttime railroad track repair in front of her apartment on the fringes of New York's East Harlem wrote:

"I am not a violent person and have never had and do not expect to ever have anything to do with the riots in our cities. But having lived on the fringe of East Harlem for 1-1½ years I am in a position to begin to understand riots and the reasons for them, and even to sympathize with them. . . . If I were a Negro and had I lived in Harlem always I might be more violent than they have been or ever shall be . . . . Residents have been forced to endure the penetrating noise . . . and to rise or stay up all night because the noise is so intense.

"If the New York Central Railroad could be bombed with fire bombs or dynamite, or a fire started, without any loss of life, and if I were a native of Harlem, I might turn my lack of cooperation by the authorities into destructive retaliation . . . . At times one has to take things into his own hands, when he has had enough, and has exhausted other means, and use whatever means is available to him."

Someday, we shall be able to count the dollar cost of noise, and diagnose its price in physical health. But, in trying to assay a direct dollar cost, we must not lose sight of the fact that this life on earth is a limited one. Noise, no matter how one interprets its impact, does "cost" man a portion of his human existence. I am haunted by the phrase environmentalist Ron Linton used before a meeting of the American Public Health Association: "What is the cost of a living day?"

PART III

Acoustic Anarchy

CHAPTER SIX

No Legal Recourse

In 1930 the first Noise Abatement Commission in the United States, appointed by the New York City Health Department, filed a report that has become a classic. It could be republished today with only a few minor changes, like substituting jets and air conditioners for street cars and ice deliveries. Its description of the problem and suggested solutions are just as timely today as they were four decades ago, proof that commissions are just paper tigers without government commitment backing them up.

An anti-noise committee established by New York's Mayor Robert F. Wagner in 1955, and sponsored by the NYC Department of Commerce and Public Events, conducted its own noise poll (see Table 2). Comparing its results with those of 1930, the 1955 Committee concluded: "In three decades little has changed except the order of priority." Today in 1970 the public still complains about virtually the same noises. We still have acoustic laissez-faire.

TABLE 2

THE NOISES THAT WON'T GO AWAY:
PUBLIC SURVEYS OF MOST ANNOYING SOUNDS—
NEW YORK CITY
In Order Of Priority

1956*	1926**
1. Refuse collection	1. Trucks
2. Hornblowing	2. Automobile horns
3. Acceleration of motors	3. Radios
4. Blaring of radio and TV sets	4. Elevated trains
5. Aircraft noise	5. Automobile brakes and cut-outs
6. Unmuffled exhausts	6. Garbage collections
7. Street repairs	7. Street cars
8. Sound trucks	8. Fire Department sirens
9. Construction riveting	9. Noisy parties and entertainment
10. Doormen's whistles	10. Milk and ice deliveries

* Conducted in cooperation with the New York *World Telegram and Sun*. The list was printed as a coupon in the newspaper. Categories for the list were taken from letters and telephone calls received by the Committee.

** Adapted to conform to the categories used by the Committee for a Quiet City, Inc. Other noises voted most annoying in 1926 included riveting, dogs and cats, horse-drawn trucks, pneumatic drills, and traffic whistles.

Source: *Final Report and Recommendations* of the Committee for a Quiet City, Inc., July 7, 1960.

The Constitution sets safeguards for the sanctity of a man's home from unlawful invasion. These safeguards do not apply to noise, and the right to privacy is one of the sacrifices we make for the benefits of speed and convenience.

When it comes to noise assault the city dweller is disenfranchised. Judges consistently have ruled that when one agrees to live in a city he agrees to accept any and all noise that goes with city living. This makes a joke of the Quiet Enjoyment clause found in apartment house leases, ". . . the Tenant shall quietly enjoy the leased premises." Today's noises have deleted this clause as effectively as if it were xx'd out and initialed by land-lord and tenant.

In most cases, you can't sue. You don't even have the right to stop the overhead neighbor's son from pounding away with a full complement of drums and amplified rock'n'roll instruments. When his $400-a-month tenants threatened to move out, one Manhattan landlord tried to evict a young drummer's family. The judge ruled: "While the court can sympathize with the neighbors who may be annoyed by the sound of the drums, that is the price they must pay to live in a city apartment." He referred to children learning to make music as some of the more civilized sounds of life.

The Industrial Revolution gave business and industry great power—including the right to pollute, the right of the machine to be as noisy as it is today. This state of things typically means that the maker of machines is free to choose his design goals, and must not be pressured by laws or ordinances to spend time or money for quiet.

Society seems to look upon any degree of excessive noise as it now regards pornography—if it contains a modicum of social value, it is not obscene.

For example, most cities do not regulate the noise levels of air conditioners. As long as the apparatus is operating properly, judges will not recognize a noisy air conditioner as a nuisance. In a precedent-setting case, one court ruled that an air condi-tioner is a product of man's search for improved comfort and enjoyment, and the fact that it may cause some annoyance to others does not justify denouncing its use as criminal.

Certain magic words can ward off any meaningful regulation. These words are: socially useful, temporary, and mobile. Many communities have adopted the model anti-noise code recommended by the National Institute of Municipal Law Officers. Written to cover "unnecessary and unreasonable" noise, it is a license to pollute. Here is part of the "preamble" to New York City's "model" anti-noise ordinance:

"Unnecessary noises: Prohibited. a. Subject to the provisions of this section, the creation of any unreasonably loud, disturbing, and unnecessary noise is prohibited. . . ."

That word *unnecessary* is the fly in the ointment. It is not interpreted as meaning capable of being designed to make less noise, or capable of being muffled. An unnecessary noise is a noise without social utility. Dog barking and promiscuous use of the auto horn are deemed to be without social utility. Construction noise is the result of a socially useful activity, and therefore free from restraint.

Daytime construction noise is specifically exempt from regulation. All municipalities that have adopted the model code contain a clause similar to this one, found in the New York City Administrative Code, prohibiting "the erection, including excavating, demolition, alteration or repair of any building other than between seven ante meridian and six post meridian on weekdays, except in case of urgent necessity in the interest of public safety and then only with a permit from the commissioner of buildings, which permit may be renewed for a period of three days or less while the emergency continues."

This is acoustic anarchy with a vengeance. Any degree of construction noise can be legally maintained from 7:00 A.M. to 6:00 P.M. (and through the night with an easily obtained permit), six days a week (and Sunday by permit), week in and week out for many months and years. It is noise legally defined as temporary and necessary and thus excluded from the laws of nuisance.

It is, for example, the intense noise generated by giant portable air compressors that force-feed the jackhammers with enough pressure to enable them to slug away with 1,100 80-pounds-per-square-inch blows per minute, while exuding waste energy to the tune of 105 or more decibels. It is noise made by the giraffe-like pneumatic rock drills employed to drill holes for dynamite charges. It is the incredible noise made by another pneumatic tool, the tamper or compactor used to beat down the soil or for subsurfacing. One model, the "Jumping-Jack," delivers a 1,000-pound sock at the rate of 350 to 700 blows per minute. Its cousin, heavyweight "Wallopin' Whale," delivers 3,400- to 6,000-pound blows at the rate of 1,500 to 2,000 per minute. Construction equipment is not designed for human compatibility.

Not only do the air compressors and jackhammers not have to be muffled, neither do the cranes, bulldozers, or transit cement mixers.

Existing ordinances permit daytime mayhem, and do little to protect sleep. If a businessman or a contractor makes a good case for nighttime work, claiming inconvenience or loss of money if he must restrict his operation to daytime hours, city officials can permit such extended activities.

The city has the authority to permit highway and building demolition and construction work at any hour of the night. This permission is granted in Memphis, supposedly the most noise-conscious city in the United States, if the contractor claims he will suffer "loss or inconvenience" if restricted to the daylight hours of 7:00 A.M. to 6:00 P.M., and if the chief building inspector determines that "the public health and safety will not be impaired."

Municipal governments could protect their citizens via their licensing power. Private garbage carters are licensed by the cities in which they operate. Silenced operations could be a licensing prerequisite, or at least, unsilenced garbage trucks could be issued licenses that deny them the right to operate after 11:00 P.M. But instead of requiring silenced garbage trucks and quiet garbage receptacles, the New York City Department of Licenses sent out this ineffective regulation:

NOTICE TO THE CARTING INDUSTRY

Numerous noise complaints are received daily by this Department with regard to carting activities between the hours of 11:00 P.M. and 7:00 A.M.

We are aware of the problems involved in restricting carting service to the daytime hours. You are, therefore, directed to eliminate all disturbing noise during the hours of 11:00 P.M. and 7:00 A.M. This includes:

1. Loud and boisterous discussion
2. Banging of pails and covers
3. Grinding of noisy compaction machinery

The health ar.d welfare of the residents of this City are the prime consideration of this department at all times.

Failure to heed this directive will result in an order for all cartmen not to operate during these restricted hours.

The Department knows full well that today's garbage trucks are 100-decibel noisemakers. This type of regulation is nothing but window dressing.

Since there are no protective ordinances or regulations allowing at least an extra hour of sleep, let us say to 8:00 A.M., political influence is helpful. When a Cambridge student was awakened at 7:00 A.M. by the grinding of an English "dust lorry" plus the dustman's off-key rendition of "O, Come All Ye Faithful," he got corrective action. The dustman was instructed not to pick up until 8:00 A.M. The student happened to be Prince Charles.

New York's Greenwich Village residents, who have fought coffeehouse noise unsuccessfully will appreciate Miami's answer to similar noise emissions. Its city code prohibits "between the hours of 11:00 P.M. and 7:00 A.M. music, singing or other forms of entertainment in any room where beer, wine, liquor or al-

coholic beverages are sold or offered for sale, indoors or outdoors, unless such room is soundproofed in order that the noise
therefrom may not disrupt the peace and quiet of the neighborhood. . . . "

This requirement—that a place of amusement keep its noise
to itself—is so sensible, yet few communities avail themselves of
it.

Society exempts noisemaking activities that come under the
category of "temporary." Unfortunately for the public, construction noise falls into this category.

The noise experts omitted construction noise from a 1967
symposium on noise sponsored by the Acoustical Society of
America because, explained the Chairman of its Noise Technical
Committee, "construction noise is temporary."

"Temporary" can be one, two, five years, or more.

Life, too, is temporary.

There is an irrational double standard that applies to fixed
installations such as factories. Noise created inside factories is
sometimes limited by zoning laws, but *mobile* "factories" such
as garbage trucks, fuel trucks that pump oil into homes, re-
frigerated trucks, are not covered by decibel limitations even
though the noise they generate affects residential areas much
more directly. "Objectionable industrial noise," reported the
American Society of Planning Officials, designers of the performance standards for zoning codes, "is overwhelmingly due to
traffic and transportation noises—trucks coming from and going
to the plant, steam locomotives puffing and diesel engines thun-
dering, box cars switching and gondolas banging, thousands
of self-propelled employees changing shifts. The chance of controlling this type of noise through a performance standard on
noise generation is not good." It is conceivable that a community zoning code would control the noise of rockets being
built inside a factory, but would exempt the noise of rocket

engine tests if the testing occurred outside the plant.

Zoning laws, in their failure to cover aircraft operations and construction noise, are indeed limited in effectiveness. "Mobile industries seem to consider themselves privileged as far as noise is concerned," complains Jim Botsford, who is Bethlehem Steel's Noise Control Engineer. "They argue they are vital to the economy and the public interest. [But they are] no more so than many industries fixed to real estate . . . . There is no valid reason why local business should be required to 'shut up or shut down' at night while trucks and airplanes are allowed to roar through until dawn."

The noise-harassed citizen is not even permitted the essential of quiet living space. The misconception that a decent acoustic environment is a luxury rather than a necessity and a human right, plus greed and the pressure of competition, encourage the builder to ignore noise insulation. In the United States there is no national code for dwelling sound control. Though such codes could be found in Europe as early as 1938, not until New York City adopted one in 1968 did a single American municipality have a building code with noise control provisions.

Since the New York code will probably be "sold" to other municipalities, it is important to understand its weaknesses.

The decibel key to a building code is a combination of three standards. The Sound Transmission Class (STC) measures the ability of the wall to keep out sound. The Impact Noise Rating (INR) describes the ability of the floor/ceiling construction to keep out sound. The Noise Criteria (NC) specify permissible sound levels in unoccupied rooms, setting limits on noises from mechanical equipment outside of the rooms, such as air conditioning, ventilating, and heating systems.

According to noise control specialist Martin Hirschorn, New York City's proposed rating for walls is below the lowest standard reported in Europe.*

---

*Some control requirements, such as the STC and the NC ratings, will be upgraded as of January 1, 1972.

Another acoustical consultant, who specified what New York City should have for floor/ceiling ratings, told the American Carpet Institute: "Impact Noise Ratings of − 2 to + 4 have been specified as minimum requirements for multifamily dwellings. These should not be considered as 'design criteria.' It has been our experience that ratings on the order of +10 to + 15 must be obtained for a reasonable degree of tenant satisfaction." By "reasonable," he said he meant 75 to 90 per cent. New York's INR of "0" can mean that perhaps 75 per cent of the tenants will *not* be satisfied.

The noise level from continuously running mechanical equipment permitted by the code is NC 40. Hirschorn told the City Council that the American Society of Heating, Refrigerating and Air-Conditioning Engineers (ASHRAE) listed NC 40 as a recommended average criterion for "halls, corridors, lobbies, laboratories, general open offices, general banking areas, restaurants, nightclubs, clothing stores, bowling alleys, gymnasiums." Said he: "A man coming home from work is surely entitled to something a little quieter. The basis of this code is the assumption that an NC 40 is acceptable to the majority of people living in city apartments; this is an incorrect assumption and, in effect, would legislate noisier apartments than we have now in this city . . . . When no standard existed he (the tenant) could complain about excessive noise . . . . Now the builders . . . would presumably have no need to modify their installation if they met the provisions of the proposed law, even though their acoustical performance might be highly disturbing to a large number of people."

The late Senator Robert F. Kennedy was concerned about the flaws in this proposed code because he realized it could become the model for city governments throughout the nation. He wrote the City Council: " . . . Passage of the code, as presently written, does not go nearly far enough towards preserving some form of peace and quiet in our cities . . . .

" . . . Provisions ought to exist for improving windows and insulation to provide for the same sound attenuation from the outside as exists between apartments. Criteria ought to be set for regulating noise within schools and hospitals as well . . . ."

This code permits noise intrusion from hallways, lobbies, and similar areas. There is no provision for the noise rating of appliances used within an apartment, the built-in appliances such as dishwashers, no provision for quiet toilets.

After waiting almost three decades, why didn't one of the world's noisiest cities adopt a more stringent code? To spare the real estate industry? Perhaps, but the *professed* reason for the poor decibel standards involves a bit of acoustic magic, the conversion of a most disturbing noise—the noise of passing motor vehicle traffic—into beneficial noise.

Here's how the code's acoustical consultant explained the low standards:

"These minimum standards have been selected with the knowledge that the apartment buildings will be located in areas of density and traffic conditions . . . where normal ambient noise levels generated by concentrated vehicle activity and high density occupancy will provide beneficial masking of intruding speech signals and other noises."

It is difficult to say who is responsible for this acoustic doublethink—private industry or government. But the FHA supports this "beneficial masking" concept for dwelling design:

"We must distinguish between two types of noise. The first is the ambient noise environment, the quiet, neutral, background noise from flowing traffic or air-conditioning equipment to which we rapidly become accustomed and soon do not notice at all [*sic*]. This background noise is an exceedingly important element in all noise control situations for it helps to mask the sporadic intruding sounds. For example, an intruding noise which would be intolerable in a quiet country village might go completely unnoticed in an apartment or a busy street, where the continuous hum of traffic masks out the noises from next door without itself seeming unpleasant."

The harsh fact about any anti-noise legislation is that in order

not to be attacked as "unreasonable" or "unrealistic," the decibel limits must be acceptable to commerce and industry.

Unless the law has provision for improvement with time, all
decibel legislation does is freeze an intolerable noise level in
perpetuity. Three years after enactment of the New York State
motor vehicle decibel limit in 1965, the problem was as acute as
ever. After a meeting of the state's Department of Transportation and its Thruway Authority with the Thruway Noise Abatement Committee, a publicity release was issued from the
Governor's Executive Chamber. The only new abatement measure mentioned was a review of the plan to plant trees and shrub-
bery along the right-of-way in an attempt to muffle the traffic
noise. Hundreds of feet of dense plantings would be necessary
to provide any degree of significant reduction. The highway
bisects many residential areas, leaving little or no space for such
plantings. Nothing was said about requiring Detroit to lower its
emission level.

Even as concern for environmental quality is adopted as Federal policy,* there is little evidence that excessive noise will be
taken seriously. It is Utopian to expect strict legislation against
noise because it is ugly or uncomfortable. True, until the lobby
for junkyards and billboards proved more powerful than the
lobby for aesthetics, Congress did make a try at highway beautifi-
cation. Why not money for "acoustic beauty"? Why not, indeed.
There is a world of economic difference between getting a manufacturer to landscape his factory grounds and provide litter bas-
kets, and getting him to design and re-tool for quieter appliances.
Politicians will never ban helicopters and STOLcraft from the
center of the city because they are unattractive, or because they
make unmusical sounds.

So rare is the interest in the noise problem that as a freshman

---

*The National Environmental Policy Act of 1969. Section 102 of that act re-
quires that Federal agencies report activities which would negatively influence
environmental quality.

Congressman, Theodore Kupferman made national news when he first introduced a bill calling for an Office of Noise Abatement. However, several years of active nationwide campaigning netted him little more than the support of some 50 colleagues, and his bill remained in the House Commerce Committee, burial ground of all noise bills.

Neglect is the theme of a shocking document—*"Noise: Sound Without Value"*—prepared by the Federal Council for Science and Technology and released in 1968. This report tells in detail how the administrative branch of the Federal government is aware of the growing seriousness of unregulated noise. It then documents how all that is lacking is a policy, authorization, budget, research facilities, and a coordinating noise abatement program.

Not only does society not regulate the most serious noises in the environment, it does not design that environment to provide a buffer between permanent noise sources and the public. Noise is seldom mentioned in the conferences of planners, and an expert committee of the World Health Organization has had to urge metropolitan planners to cooperate with environmental health personnel to create environments with reduced noise and vibration.

"There is is no evidence," states Canadian government noise researcher George Thiessen, "that traffic noise has had any appreciable influence on decisions made in the field of planning." Homes are built on top of busy highways, and even hospitals are not shielded from traffic noise. It was not until 1967 that the Federal government started even to consider potential noise radiation in routing the 2,500 miles of urban highway that are still to be built for the interstate highway system.

Our lives are excessively noisy because not only do city planners tend to ignore surface noise, they totally ignore noise from the sky. Though the airplane is the chief culprit, airport design and operation are important factors in the jet noise problem. Yet the airport operator is usually free of any restraints.

It is somewhat behind the times to plan for green belts as buffers from noisy factories, while leaving the residential areas the buffers are supposed to protect exposed to overhead noise from aviation.

It is not "natural" for machines to make noise, but without any incentive to do otherwise, industry assembles its machines—and buildings—to meet the more obviously rewarding goals of style (something that can be sold) and economy.

Poorly designed gears, imperfectly designed and installed bearings, improperly designed air flow used to cool rotating parts —these are some of the "unnatural" reasons mechanized products produce noise. To add acoustic insult to industrial tightfistedness, light-weight metal has been substituted for enclosures made of heavy cast iron. These light-weight covers are "excited" by the poorly balanced, poorly insulated motors of dishwashers and air compressors alike, and in turn vibrate and generate additional noise.

Without legal restraints, air conditioners provide thermal comfort at the cost of acoustic discomfort. Without regulation, our subways climb above 90 decibels, as noisy as heavy trucks at 20 feet and train whistles at 500 feet. Subway noise complaints are as much a part of American life as apple pie and Girl Scout cookies. And though Americans hear little about railroad noise these days, Canadian experts describe railroad trains as the noisiest form of surface transportation.

Acoustic anarchy is the only description for motor vehicle operation. In the United States there are neither national regulations nor national guidelines for what is patently a problem of interstate commerce. Only two states, New York and California, have adopted decibel limits, in both cases too high. A handful of North American cities have specified noise maxima, but these are either too high or of doubtful legality. Milwaukee, which is often cited for its excellent decibel law, had as a matter of record to rescind its ordinance in 1957, because its Municipal Court ruled that the use of decibel meters was unconstitutional. Toronto enacted a decibel law which held up in the courts, but because of a technicality, enforcement was restricted to one, and only one, sound-measuring instrument. Hampered by this restriction, Toronto police use the traditional guide of "unreasonable noise" as an enforcement basis.

Famous for enforcing its motor vehicle muffler and horn laws, Memphis does not have an ordinance concerning the use of the sound meter; however, the city court judges have accepted the police department's criteria of 90 decibels for automobiles and 100 decibels for trucks. The permitted noise levels are so high, judges need have no qualms the noisemakers would be unable to meet them easily.

The absence of effective standards allows 40 per cent of the trucks on New York's highways to generate excessive noise. More than 50 per cent of the trucks in the midtown New York City area were reported by an acoustician to have noisy engines and poor mufflers.

Not only does society permit inadequate muffling of motor vehicles, it totally ignores the other sources of automotive noise. General Motors publishes a silencing manual for the guidance of purchasers of its trucks and motors. The manual notes that truck operators need concern themselves only with mufflers, since laws do not cover engine noise and other vehicular noise sources.

One of the noise sources ignored by regulations is the auto horn. There are no maximum standards for horn emissions. In France, automobiles are equipped with a Country Horn and a quieter City Horn. In the United States, Chrysler Corp. specifies a limit for its horns: the sound level as measured at 4 inches from the horn shall be *at least* 125 decibels!

Without insistence on proper design, increase in power becomes synonymous with increase in noise. One reason for the jet noise problem is the escalation from the 12,000-pound-thrust DC-3 to the 41,000 pounds of thrust generated by the subsonic jets. The combined roar of jet exhaust, whine of jet compressors, and sounds of the turbines, generates more than 140 decibels at takeoff. Homes near airports may experience exposures of more than 100 decibels. Community complaints may begin at 90, and explode at 105!

Without people-oriented controls, the best that will happen is a freeze at levels undesirable to begin with, or an insignificant reduction. The airline industry is satisfied that its giant air buses will be no louder, perhaps an insignificant few decibels quieter, than current models. This satisfaction with maintaining the noisy status quo is also found in the air conditioning industry where air conditioner manufacturers are proud to tell the public that new, more powerful units are no noisier than the older, less powerful ones.

Though cities have the major responsibility for noise control, they do not have the authority to control most of the major noise sources. The Federal government, for example, has pre-empted air navigation and air traffic, and any noise limits (other than on the ground) must be set by a Federal agency. When the Village of Cedarhurst, Long Island, adjoining Kennedy Airport, tried to prohibit aircraft flights over itself at heights of less than 1,000 feet, it was overruled in the courts. When the Federal government failed to come up with noise limits, Ralph G. Caso, the Presiding Supervisor of the Town of Hempstead, also next to Kennedy Airport, took a more sophisticated tack. In self-defense against the low overflights from the pattern of takeoffs and landings, an ordinance was enacted that limited aircraft noise to an average level approximately that of trucks at 50 feet. To keep aircraft from being fined, suit was brought in 1963 by the Port of New York Authority, the airlines, and the FAA. Hempstead lost in the Federal courts because, in effect, the town ordinance would restrict the use of the airport and infringe on Federal regulation of air commerce.

If someone ran back and forth over your lawn or dashed through your living room, sometimes once a minute, and at any

time of the day or night, you could have him arrested for trespassing. A plane flying twenty feet over your backyard is not
trespassing. Not according to law. Trespass has been ruled out
because the Supreme Court has said (*U.S. vs. Causby*) that land
ownership is limited. Until that ruling, the owner of a piece of
land acquired "*ad coelum*" ownership, ownership to the sky.
This type of unrestricted ownership has no place in the modern
world. Declared the Court, "The airspace apart from the immediate reaches above the land is part of the public domain." In
effect, the airspace over one's property needed for the takeoff
and landing of aircraft is navigable airspace, an aerial highway
that cannot be restricted either by an individual or by the community.

If you raise chickens next to an airport, and the overflights are
so low and so frequent as to cause your chickens to panic and
kill themselves by dashing themselves against the walls of their
pens, your constitutional rights have been denied—*also* by ruling in the case of *U.S. vs. Causby*. You can't get the planes to
make less noise or fly higher or elsewhere. You can, however, be
reimbursed for the dead chickens. You must then go and raise
your chickens somewhere else. One farmer whose wife was
given headaches because of low and frequent overflights, went
to court and won damages to cover the cost of the aspirins.

It's not absolutely necessary to own chickens. If your home is
made untenable because of low and frequent flights and you can
prove a reduction in property values, you can sometimes win
damages. But you may have to move to prove that your home
is unlivable.

It is a sad commentary on our way of life that the signs of a
successful airport operation are the abandoned homes and
schools that surround the facility.

Health agencies have shown little or no concern for environmental noise. As a consequence, most municipal and state health
departments—including that of the largest city in the United

States—have neither the authority, the equipment, nor the personnel to cope with the noise problem.

Yet the typical municipal anti-noise ordinance contains this type of statement: "Noise of such character, intensity, and duration as to be detrimental to the life or health of any individual is prohibited."

This would seem to place abatement in the hands of the health department. Not necessarily. As in other areas of bureaucratic concern, buckpassing is the rule of the day. Consider the following:

On April 26, 1965, without any advance warning, my doorbell rang, and I admitted a cherubic Health Inspector, Mr. B. He told me he was especially qualified to listen to noise complaints, because he had once written a term paper on noise, and on weekends he moonlighted as a musician. "I am interested in noise because I am a musician," he said. "I personally recognize noise as a health problem or I wouldn't be here." I could have wept for joy at meeting my first sympathetic official.

Mr. B. listened attentively, as —shouting into his ear to make myself heard over the noise from the construction site below my windows—I suggested the TA be told a health problem existed, that muffling was necessary, or at least some reduction of the operating time of nine hours. Although he told me that the Health Department could not pressure another government agency, it just wasn't done, he smilingly promised some kind of action, and disappeared into the bureaucratic maze.

Three months later, two more Health Department inspectors appeared, listened stolidly, and disappeared. They were not musicians.

After waiting a week or so, I called the Health Department. I was curious. I wanted to know what, if anything, was happening, and what instrument that first inspector played. Whoever I talked to told me nothing could be done about my problem. He then complained bitterly of construction noise outside the Health Department building. Not only that, he told me sadly, but he hadn't been sleeping at night because of heavy trucks passing under the windows of his Third Avenue apartment. Automatically switching roles, I promised I'd see what I could do for him, and hung up. I was getting to feel sorry for the members of the Health Department, working in such a noisy city.

Four months later, one of the brass in the Sanitary Section of the Health Department told me the Department *is* concerned and *could* act under the Administrative Code's anti-noise section, or under the Sanitary Code's nuisance provision. But my joy was short-lived, because he said regretfully that since construction noise was exempt from the ordinance, I would have to go to court and have a judge hang the label "nuisance" on the air compressors and the rest of the construction apparatus.

One day, the Health Department musician mysteriously reappeared. This time he came in response to my complaint about the operation of a noisy hoist engine, one of two on the site of a new office building being erected just a stone's throw away from my apartment. He heard the gadget's piercing whine, agreed it was a nuisance, and said he would so notify his superiors and the contractor. He left me in uplifted spirits, this time never to return. But not until he ended one frustration, and told me it was the violin he played.

Ten days later a staff member of the Health Department informed me, by telephone, that noise nuisance is no concern of that Department. Seven days later this man's superior informed me the Department did have an interest in noise, and there would be followup action. On one condition: the motor operating the hoist must be defective.

On February 11, 1966, my Health Department contact phoned to tell me that one of the two hoist engines was noisier than the other. My hopes were quickly dashed, though, when he added the information that although noisier, it was ruled *not* a nuisance. However, the Health Department, in a touching gesture of humaneness, did ask the operator to try to quiet the noisier engine. On March 11 this same contact informed me that the Corporation Counsel had cautioned the Health Department to go easy on noise nuisance because of a lack of standards. Also, one of the inspectors who had visited my apartment and the site had reported that in his opinion no nuisance existed.

I did find out that in 1959 the New York City Health Department had transferred all but one reference to noise from the Sanitary Code to the Administrative Code, to be enforced by the Police Department. "Too many complaints," was the reason I was given. No wonder the Health Department could tell me: "One thousand complaints about noise mean nothing to us. We will help you only if you take your complaint to court and the judge rules it is a nuisance. It's up to the judge to say what's a nuisance, not the Heath Department."

Is it entirely fair to criticize agencies such as the Transit Authority and the FAA for ignoring the public's well-being when health officials do the same? Men who run transportation agencies are not physicians, sociologists, or ecologists. They think primarily in terms of getting things done at the lowest possible cost to their interests. But the commissioner of health in a large city is a man with a wealth of training and experience in medicine and/or preventive medicine.

Health departments came into existence after cholera had killed so many people that the public became aroused. There were no scientific standards 100 years ago, just some common-sense working standards which gave the public health people the power to act without waiting for proof of harm. Today's health departments are content to cope with impure milk and communicable diseases. The only damage to health acknowledged by city health departments is hearing loss experienced after long years of exposure to industrial noise levels. This unrealistic view comes from defining the effect of twentieth-century noise in terms of nineteenth-century medicine.

State health departments are no better. When I exhausted my attempts to get any action from the city health department, I tried some state health departments and found the same neglect. For example, when in 1963 New Jerseyites complained about noise of industrial plants, commercial air conditioners, truck terminals, railroad freight yards and airports, citing interference with sleep, with eating, and "life in general was made miserable," the State Health Department took the position that, "Evaluated against today's standards, these noises are not health hazards. They do not directly produce disease." Perhaps not directly, but how about indirectly?

As for the U.S. Public Health Service, even as late as 1970 it had no community noise program, no guidelines to offer, not even funds for thorough noise surveys.

A point about noise as a nuisance. The San Francisco police, and police of other cities, will arrest prostitutes as nuisances. Nuisance is defined as "something injurious to the health" and "offensive to the senses." The spirochete and the gonococcus can be seen under the microscope; therefore they exist. The decibel is invisible. A prostitute offends the community's sensitivities; the raucous truck, the jet, and the jackhammer do not.

Individuals complaining about disorderly or noisy neighbors frequently find the police indifferent to their complaints. But it is not only the law—both common and statutory—that contributes to the current state of acoustic anarchy; it is the attitude of the courts as well. Just as judges are reluctant to convict for disorderly conduct under the Penal Code, they seem reluctant to convict for any type of noise offense.

It would have been a waste of time to seek a court ruling that the subway project was a nuisance, for another reason. Since the ordinance makes an exception of construction noise, to ask for a ruling of nuisance would be asking a judge to disregard the exemption. Courts are reluctant to take the lead in noise abatement. Though liberal lawyers have argued that the courts have a responsibility to protect the public from noise assault, some jurists reply that it is not for the courts to supplant legislators. "The community must have adequate laws and regulations," they contend, "and not depend upon the courts to act as substitutes."

It is possible that higher courts might take a more progressive view of noise nuisance. But very few noise cases get to be judged on substance. Most, because of lack of funds for appeals, are blocked on legal technicalities by the court of first jurisdiction.

As far as the effectiveness of common law to control noise is concerned, one cannot but agree with the conclusion of David Watts, a New York University law student who wrote a paper on noise and the law: "It is obvious that nuisance law does not adequately cope with noise. Therefore it is appropriate to consider the use of anti-noise ordinances." But, as we have seen, the anti-noise ordinances exonerate the major noise nuisances.

New York City's Police Commissioner Howard Leary gave me the official legal philosophy adopted by his Department in enforcing existing noise restrictions:

> It is generally agreed that in noise abatement cases, the courts have concluded that each person must put up with a certain amount of annoyance, inconvenience and interference. In addition, the courts have ruled that in determining the amount of annoyance, inconvenience and interference that must be tolerated, the gravity of the harm to the complainant should be weighed against the utility of the conduct of his troublesome neighbor.

Since not all noisy acts are listed in ordinances, police must judge if an act unspecified by their town's law is a violation. If they are familiar with the "gravity-*vs.*-utility" doctrine, they are not likely to proceed against a noise that they do not believe is detrimental to health and life. Since the only recognized health damage is hearing loss from years of industrial-type exposure, it is not surprising that police do not get excited about noise in the community.

Discussing a nighttime utility jackhammmer complaint, one desk sergeant put it this way: "So I send a car and the men ask to see a permit. The crew says they forgot it. We check the next night, and it's a new crew. So what if we give a summons? The penalty is so small that it means nothing to the utility.

Most judges throw these cases out anyway."

Reluctance to enforce the ban on promiscuous horn blowing is blamed on the strict laws of evidence. A New York policeman explained to me: "If I give a summons and go to court, where I may have to spend a whole day, the judge asks the guy if he blew his horn unnecessarily. The guy can say he blew it because he thought a cat was crossing the street in front of him. Or the judge can give me the third degree: did I actually see this driver put his pinky on his horn? Did I actually see that horn button or ring depressed? It's like with prostitutes—the case gets thrown out for lack of evidence."

One of the most touching excuses for not enforcing a decibel limit for motor vehicles was that given by one English police chief. He felt that enforcing motor vehicle noise laws would deteriorate the relationship between the police and the motoring public!

Legend has it that the gods once drowned man for making too much noise. According to the story, the Babylonian god Eulil, like a minister of justice, prosecuted man for his sins. "The sins of mankind have not decreased, but increased. *Their noises have stirred my anger.*" The prosecution won its case and the gods decided to drown a noisy mankind—more than 4,000 years before the advent of noisy trucks and jets. Thus the Babylonians explained the Great Flood.

But modern lawmakers, more lenient than those ancient noise abatement gods, let the noisemakers go free. In the eyes of our government we, the public, the people who consume, who produce, who pay the taxes and make the personal sacrifices necessary for our nation's survival, are not worthy of a quieter city, suburb, farm, school, or hospital. Not if it means disturbing the manufacturer and operator of noisy machines. The problem is not so much how to fight City Hall, but why it should be necessary to fight City Hall in the first place.

CHAPTER SEVEN

The Politics Of Noise

The Industrial Revolution destroyed one culture and replaced it with another, in the name of economic necessity. Modern technology is destroying livability for the same reason. The problem of noise is seen as a balancing of business interests against the interests of a suffering public, except that business is identified with "the public," and ordinary people, the victims, are left out in the noisy cold.

Noise abatement is presented not as an essential, but a luxury. "Our most troublesome noise problems carry price tags," states acoustic authority Leo Beranek, Ph.D.. "Economic considerations must be weighed against people's desires for culture and the 'good life.' "

The rights of the individual must give way to the new interpretation of public interest. Karl Kryter emphasized this in relation to community reaction to jet noise, when he stated: "It is obvious that air transportation brings benefits to the community at large

141

and that air transportation is an important part of our economy and way of life. Perhaps the annoyance and disturbance suffered by some is the price that must be paid."

When towns outside of New York City fought a fourth jetport, *The New York Times* considered them selfish. It editorialized, "Sympathetic as we are to the desire of local residents everywhere to escape the battered eardrums that go with a nearby jetport, one must be built for the welfare of the entire metropolitan complex of 17 million people."

To protest against large chunks of desirable living space being pre-empted by noisy "progress," is deemed reactionary. *Aviation Week* takes a dim view of those who oppose center-city aviation: "The attempt to bring a V/STOL type of air transport even deeper into the heart of communities than existing airports will certainly encounter formidable opposition of citizen groups, city councils, county boards, state legislatures and federal agencies bristling with reasons to stop the clock of airline progress." (I wish I were as certain as this editor that government would be on the side of the public.)

We are now living in a world where to object to excessive noise is to get oneself labeled unpatriotic. When Manhattan residents complained of late-hour parade noises, the veterans' organization sponsoring the event questioned their patriotism. Mayor Lindsay had to make a personal appearance to soothe ruffled feathers when the indignant veterans resolved never to convene in New York again.

New York City Councilman Robert Low received an unexpected response when he stopped the operator of a noisy cement mixer to speak of his interest in construction-noise legislation. He was rebuffed with an angry outcry: "You trying to lose me my job? You some kind of a Communist nut?"

According to a story in the *Wall Street Journal*, "Anyone who objects to the SST's noise is left feeling somehow unpatriotic—and provincial." The story went on to quote the Director of the FAA's Office of Supersonic Transport Development, Air Force

Major General J. C. Maxwell: "Americans must recognize that the airplane will benefit not only the people of the United States but the entire world as well."

The FAA is aware of the power of belief in the "price of progress" doctrine to win jet noise acceptance. Its propaganda stresses the benefits of an airport as a revenue-producing commercial center generating millions of dollars in payrolls, thus making the interests of the airport and the community mutual. The Port of New York Authority, operator of four jetports, warns that New York City's position as the financial and economic center of the world depends, in part, upon making it convenient for business executives to travel between New York and other cities.

To counter critics of round-the-clock flights, the FAA painted a dark economic picture of what would happen if restrictions were applied: "Banning night flights would be one sure way of eliminating some aircraft noise (but) . . . it would retard the normal growth of business; put a great many people out of work; seriously cut local payrolls; and otherwise adversely affect the welfare of the very community which seeks to impose the restrictions."

In 1961 the FAA published a brochure, "Sounds of the Twentieth Century." To make the public think the government cared, this brochure stated: "The Federal Aviation Agency, the aircraft and engine manufacturers, airlines, pilots, and airport operators are keenly aware of the disturbance that aircraft noise may cause to the people who live close to airports." It further added that the "independent" National Aircraft Noise Abatement Council was going to work hard to find "an acceptable solution to this difficult and complex problem."

Aware that many persons are frightened by jet noise, the FAA offered the reassurance: " . . . A lack of understanding of how aircraft operate causes many people to be alarmed when they see and hear aircraft land or take off. This in turn, like many things that are strange to us, can easily arouse fear. By its very nature fear causes resentment and stress. This can be alleviated, how-ever, by a better understanding of modern aircraft which are larger and often appear to be closer than they are to an observer on the ground. Modern jet aircraft . . . are remarkably reliable."

Not only did the FAA try to eradicate fear, it tried to inculcate a favorable attitude toward jet noise: "The sound of our own aircraft engines can be as reassuring to us as they were to the people of West Germany during the Berlin Airlift. America's air power . . . includes our air traffic control system, our network of Federal airways . . . and all of civil aviation . . . . We must never lose sight of the importance of civil aviation to our national defense."

The FAA has made strong emotional appeals for nighttime flights, such as: "Many people have rushed by air at night to the bedside of seriously ill friends and relatives when other trans-portation would have been too slow. Lives have been saved because a surgeon could fly at night from one part of the country to another . . . ."

Though years have passed since this public relations program was started, and complaints keep escalating, the belief in the efficacy of public relations to minimize complaints continues. When the FAA conducted tests of public reaction to sonic booms in Oklahoma City, the complaints were substantial. Part of the negative reaction is blamed by the FAA not on the sonic boom but on a poor public relations job. Major General Maxwell, then the FAA's SST program director, is quoted as saying: "We [shall] need to do a much better job of selling the SST story in the years ahead."

Faced with mounting protests, and with the expected increase of complaints from the larger jets and the sonic boom, a new Federal interagency aviation noise committee is urging a new and stronger public relations program. It is recommending that steps be taken to mitigate opposition to jet noise at the grassroots level. It further advises that preparations be made to counter the expected reaction to noise when the government releases "noise contours" which will show the noise levels at various distances from the major airports. The substance of the counterattack is to be an educational program enumerating all the "positive" things being done to tackle the problem of jet noise.

In all fairness to the FAA, it must be said that the aviation industry, too, is preparing to squelch complaints with public relations. In 1968 the international association of airline operators called a special public relations conference in Rio de Janeiro. The aviation industry was told that public relations was the best strategy for dealing with the jet noise problem. Not hit-or-miss public relations, but a thorough, full-scale continuous campaign that would try to nip complaints in the bud, or, if that failed, to de-fuse any explosive buildups. The airline representatives were told to be on the alert for murmurings of discontent in local communities and prepared to move quickly before unrest became organized and vocal. Organized action was to be forestalled by evolving a scheme for paying attention to individual complaints. If that failed, there should be an industry community council which would enable the community leaders to sit down with the airlines and be told what was being done to alleviate the problem. The community leaders would also be invited to explore with the airlines ways of improving the situation.

Public relations can make a temporary and unavoidable intense noise somewhat more bearable, but should not serve as a propaganda device to justify and continue a policy of unlimited noise. As when former Secretary of Transportation Alan Boyd said we must accept jet noise because we have accepted, having failed to silence them, trucks and railroads. Or when L. M. Tondel Jr., a lawyer member of a Federal jet noise alleviation panel, states: "The airport noise problem is not unique. Noise is also an unfortunate concomitant of garbage collection, trucks, pile drivers, riveters, pneumatic drills, sirens, sound trucks, heavy trucks and buses, small sports cars, freeways, even radios, television sets and garbage disposal units."

To implement the "complaint squelch" program, aviation has

prepared color motion picture films and elaborate colored slides and charts. "Why It Must Be Noisy" programs are available through local FAA noise abatement offices. These offices are listed in the telephone book, and the public can complain any day of the week. It can also complain to an electronic answering service on weekends and at night.

To sap your will to fight a new noise source, developers seek to create a feeling of inevitability. Road builders and public officials who route new roads next to people's homes cut down complaints by telling the community how important the road is, and at the same time reduce their will to fight it with the pronouncement that the road will be built no matter what. Paul Borsky, a leading noise survey specialist, spells out the effectiveness of such brainwashing: "If he feels the noise is inevitable, and unavoidable, and that the road is important and necessary, he will want to ignore the noise and continue about his business."

Not all brainwashing is conducted by the giants of transportation and construction. A trade association of private garbage collectors wants the public to know it cares. It adorns the sides of 100-decibel trucks with the slogan: "Shh. People are sleeping."

The failure to regulate industrial noise is a scandal that will someday rock the country. In 1968, outgoing Secretary of Labor Willard Wirtz drew up a regulation specifying a maximum noise exposure of 85 decibels that would have to be met by industries with government contracts in excess of $10,000. Industry regarded this proposal as extremely restrictive, and got the ear of the new Secretary of Labor, George Schultz. He established a review committee consisting primarily of representatives of industry, and medical men and others friendly to industry. The final number adopted was 90 decibels, instead of 85. It is claimed that ten per cent of the work force will lose its ability to hear the spoken word under these "improved" provisions. Unfortunately, there is no way of knowing who that ten per cent will be until they start to lose their hearing. Even then this will go undetected unless there is an on-going hearing testing program, something unlikely in the small factories that employ 80 per cent of the work force of the nation.

Even *Fortune* Magazine (October 1969) was critical of the new regulations, pointing out that millions of workers in plants with fewer than 20 workers and less than $10,000 in contracts would be excluded, and that the 90 dB(A) noise limit was "5 dB(A) more than the experts regarded as safe."

One would have imagined that after the 1948 Slawinski case, industry would have embarked on a program of all-out noise control. After all, in that historic ruling the courts for the first time recognized that noise-induced hearing loss was compensable. And industry was petrified, fearful of an avalanche of lawsuits. The period immediately following that historic decision was called "the industrial noise crisis."

But instead of reducing its noisy status quo, industry embarked on a program of noise liability reduction that was quite analogous to a program of reducing noise complaints instead of noise.

Physicians developed a category of hearing loss called "hearing impairment." This was an extreme degree of hearing loss, and it was further qualified in workmen's compensation laws to meet a medico-legal definition of liability. Special conditions of exposure had to be met before a case of deafness, as defined, could be charged to on-the-job exposure.

The compensation criteria are worth examining. The first rule is that the employee must have worked a certain number of years in employment exceeding arbitrary "damage-risk" noise levels, usually 8 hours a day above 85 decibels.

For purposes of disability compensation, the damage must be so extensive as to seriously impair hearing for speech. Only a hearing impairment as officially defined is recognized as a disability.

Under the New York State Workmen's Compensation Law, to

qualify for an award, not only must the hearing show a loss below 2,000 cps, but that loss must be substantial.

Industry's 2,000 cps bare-bones-of-speech criterion appears harsh even for workers, let alone the general population. How harsh is revealed by the case of a man in New York City, who worked for 44 years in the noisy pressroom of a newspaper at exposure over the damage-risk level, but could not qualify for compensation. Though three specialists diagnosed his hearing loss as severe, it was in the 4,000 cps range, and not 2,000 cps and under. So though his loss, according to the three otologists, handicapped his ability to hear all of the sounds of speech, especially some consonant sounds, he was not deaf by definition. Insurance companies and industry, influential in developing the medico-legal definitions of deafness, decide how much speech one may hear in this world.

If a worker has lost his hearing and wishes to file a claim, he must separate himself from his noisy job and wait six months. Having to wait six months discourages claims; it also encourages workers to delay making any claims until they retire. Many workers would rather knowingly grow deaf and continue working than leave for six months of idleness or transfer to a quiet but undesired job, probably with a loss of seniority and pay. "It is very unusual for a man to leave a noisy job to preserve his hearing," said a member of the Halifax Labor Department. The total number of hearing loss claims processed in the United States is relatively small; it is estimated that fewer than 500 cases were settled in 1966.

The worker who is able to separate himself from his noisy job for six months and prove he has lost a substantial amount of his hearing below 2,000 cps doesn't get too much for his pains. The states that do recognize noise-induced hearing loss set a limit on weekly payments, plus a limit on the number of weeks for which payments will be made. Michigan grants a maximum award of $28,500 for total loss of hearing in both ears, while Nebraska awards only $3,700 for the same amount of damage. For living the balance of your life unable to hear much human speech, New York State will award you a maximum weekly benefit of $80 for 60 weeks for one ear, 150 weeks for two.

There are some small touches of humanity. In Halifax, Nova Scotia, if a deafened worker has suffered a minimum of a specified noise exposure he must wait out the six months—but is entitled to a hearing aid plus reimbursement for batteries while waiting.

It is easy to understand why some experts argue that city noise will not make one deaf, if one knows that in a factory, too many minutes away from an excessively noisy machine may disqualify the operator from eventual compensation. According to theory, any temporary escape from damaging noise allows the damaged ears to recuperate. A leading industrial noise control engineer alerts employers to observe how often an employee escapes his noisy environment: "Inconspicuous interruptions could easily occur in what might appear to be a continuous exposure due to lunch periods, coffee breaks, washroom visits, occasional stoppage of machinery, etc." The sharp-eyed factory manager can reduce workmen's compensation claims not by reducing the noise level but by keeping a careful record of how much coffee his operators drank, how many cigarettes they smoked, and how often they went to the restroom.

An insurance company acoustician laughed when I told him someday construction workers would be getting workmen's compensation for hearing loss. He believes that he could prove that since the jackhammer is not operating continuously, or the operator is sometimes away from his equipment, the deafened worker could not substantiate his claim. However, government research has already shown hearing loss in road construction workers.

Too few doctors look upon excessive everyday noise exposure as undesirable. An editorial in the issue of the *Journal of the American Medical Association* for September 23, 1968, poked fun at the National Noise Study of the Public Health Service, inanely making it seem that PHS was too concerned about something that only involved a small group of industrial workers. As for the rest of the population, the editorial believed that man's ears can take it, as they always have. Some idea of the nature of this shocking piece of medical irresponsibility is found in its concluding two sentences: "The noises of the cities are the featherbeds of comfort, and noise pollution is nothing but pollution with excessive people. The quality of noise needs improvement, some think, but the quantity is only reasonable."

This type of thinking limits the health argument to industrial hearing loss. In practice there is more likelihood for political action if noise were to be recognized as a general threat to health and to the environment.

The lack of an industry-approved standard, or the decibel limit set by a standard, can determine whether or not you lose your hearing, sleep properly, or can live a life of minimum acoustic stress.

Few legislative bodies will enact regulatory legislation without the existence of an officially approved reference standard. Industry, by dominating the standard-setting process, can prevent or delay the adoption of standards, or can see to it that any standards that are adopted are virtually meaningless.

There are today no state laws limiting occupational noise exposure. Three states—California, Washington, and Oregon—have safety orders that offer very little protection. The permitted noise levels are too high; emphasis is on the use of ear protectors, and not on engineering methods for noise reduction.

More typical is the lack of any limitation. The Pennsylvania Department of Health in 1966 could report that though it had twenty years of experience with industrial noise surveys, it had not succeeded in getting legislation which would impose standards on industry. All it could do was moralize with the factory operators.

Free men are treated no worse than convicts. Workers in the Federal prison factories—Leavenworth's wooden furniture shops, the Terre Haute woolen textile mills, and the Lewisburg metal shops—are deafened by the noisy workshops. In a 24-month comparison study of various types of Federal prison workshops, the above groups experienced the greatest loss of hearing among the prisoners tested.

In the United States technical societies, trade groups, and testing organizations develop noise measurement standards and noise limits. Their umbrella organization is the private American National Standards Institute.

The organizations have standing standards committees the members of which include representatives of manufacturing concerns and insurance companies. There is some government representation, predominantly from the Department of Transportation, DOD, and NASA. It really doesn't matter whether government or private groups work on a standard. Through interlocking memberships on policy-level committees, industry pretty well controls what items will be considered for standards, what the criteria will be, if any, and how many years or decades it will take before a given standard is adopted as a "recommended practice." Delays are rationalized on the grounds of fairness to all parties, thoroughness, and the need for full agreement. Probably a more appropriate reason is that every year that goes by without a standard is considered an economic plus for industry.

According to one experienced member of standards working groups, if a standards committee cannot arrive at a set of standards in the time in which one could get a good technical college education (five years), then this group should resign. He believes there is no reason why standards cannot be set by two years from the time the working group is organized.

Though jet noise protests started in 1958, industry did nothing to set noise limits, and finally, in 1968, prodded by the Office of

Science and Technology, Congress acted, and authorized the
FAA to set noise standards.

The authorization was written in the language of the industry
itself. It said that the standards should be "economically reasonable, technologically practicable and appropriate for the particular type of aircraft . . . to which [they] will apply." These
standards, in effect, legitimize the present noise levels, for the
time being. As a matter of record, the new Boeing 747, which
is quite noisy, was exempted from the new standards because
allegedly the plans for the plane were started prior to the certifi-
cation program.

The limits of adopted standards invariably represent the noise
level produced by the equipment as manufactured. Known as
"defensive standards," they protect the manufacturer from the
cost and inconvenience of having to quiet his products. "Con-
forms to the Standards of ———" is a meaningless phrase when
applied to noise emissions.

The Society of Automotive Engineers (SAE) is consistent in
recommending the adoption of practices that will not require the
quieting of existing products. The public has no cause for rejoic-
ing in the knowledge that the SAE has a "recommended practice" for certain types of construction equipment powered by
internal combustion engines, such as bulldozers, power shovels
and cranes, compactors, or paving machines. The following exchange took place in the special hearing chamber of the New
York City Council between a councilman and a representative
of the SAE, after the SAE man testified that the recommended
decibel level for construction equipment was 90 decibels at 50
feet: "How many decibels," asked the presiding chairman,
Councilman Robert Low, "would 90 decibels be at 15 feet, the
distance at which a New Yorker would more than likely be when
passing one of those vehicles?"

The engineer stopped short, almost jabbing his aluminum
pointer through his chart. He thought for a moment, and replied
that the noise level would be something like 110 decibels.

"That's interesting," replied the councilman. "Mr. Baron and I were out this morning at a construction site and we winced at an air compressor making 95 decibels. Now you people are suggesting we legalize 110 decibels."

What the SAE had done in arriving at that standard, was to measure—with precision—the noise emissions of existing mobile construction equipment *and adopt the results as the decibel standard.*

Not only do industry standards fail their chance of promoting environmental quality and protecting human beings, but conformance to them remains voluntary. Only legislation or government regulations can force compliance.

Unfortunately, in the rare cases when a law is enacted that sets a maximum limit on noise, it refers back to these regressive industry standards. For example, the first state law setting a maximum decibel limit for motor vehicles was enacted in 1965. Adopted by New York State, this law did not acknowledge the need for adequate quiet in the homes near the thruway, but recognized industry's 1954 vehicle noise standard. In other words, at a time when noise pollution is escalating, legal limits are dictated by conditions that may have existed a decade earlier. There is no pressure on the automobile industry to produce quieter vehicles.

The consumer suffers not only from a lack of standards—and noise rating systems—he is given strange information about the noise emissions from consumer products. Take air conditioners, especially the window units. One of the most common recommendations found in mass media articles is to fight noise by switching on "the calming sounds of your air conditioner." The fact is that the American Society of Heating, Refrigerating and Air-Conditioning Engineers does not include window units in its decibel design guide—because they are too noisy. Insiders in the industry report to each other that though the public does not like the noise from air conditioners, it will *tolerate* that noise if it feels it is buying something inexpensive. To help the consumer tolerate that noise it is described as "acoustical perfume" desirable as masking for the street sounds of traffic. The latest development is to recommend air conditioner noise as a means of reducing the shock of aircraft flyovers! Small wonder that of more than 100 manufacturers of residential air conditioners, fewer than a dozen have acoustic facilities.

To forestall restrictive legislation, the industry, through its trade association, has developed its own "model" ordinance which it tries to sell to acoustically naive communities. Unnerved because Coral Gables, Florida, and Beverly Hills, California, adopted local laws calling for quiet air conditioning, the industry is now recommending that its dealers and distributors promote the model code drawn up by the American Air Conditioning and Refrigeration Institute. The editor of *Air Conditioning, Heating and Refrigeration News* has said about this code:

> Our industry's present recommended code suggests a 60-decibel level be permitted at the property line. In five years of actively monitoring the noise problem, I have yet to meet one person outside of our industry who does not consider 60 decibels an unreasonably permissive level. . . . In Cincinnati, the code authorities openly laughed at our industry's 60-decibel recommendation. . . . The industry's noise code is unrealistic.

There is no state or Federal agency in the United States to tell local civic leaders and city officials that the model code of the American Air Conditioning and Refrigeration Institute is a license to murder sleep.

The public could avoid buying excessively noisy air conditioners and appliances if it were afforded a noise rating system. Such ratings are available to military and industrial purchasing agents. One excuse the appliance industry gives for not noise-rating its consumer products is fear of a decibel war, in which one competitor will claim his product is one or two decibels quieter than those manufactured by the other guys, and consumers, presumably unaware that one decibel is not a significant difference, would favor that product. This argument must be taken with a grain of salt, if one observes the jargon about quiet in the promotion of today's noisy air conditioners. Apparently the industry would rather make it possible for all its members to exaggerate.

A decibel limit that permits intolerable noise levels in perpetuity was set some ten years ago by the Port of New York Authority for its major airports. This maximum was arrived at by determining the noise level that would be no greater than the noise produced by 75 per cent of the large four-engine propeller-driven transports; it protected the aviation industry, not the public. *Business Week* reported the words of one government official who said that this maximum "renders the surrounding area 'unfit for human habitation.' " Before this limit was introduced, people were already instituting lawsuits against propeller craft generating less noise than this limit.

Perhaps it was technologically necessary to start with an unsatisfactory limit. But what is the justification for not reducing it in the decade or more since it was introduced? Because of the sheer increase in the number of plane movements, substantial reductions in noise level would be needed to hold the line at the already intolerable existing levels.

The Port of New York Authority justifies its standard by claiming that without it, the jet noises would have been even higher. This is like telling the public it should be grateful it is living surrounded by medium cannon fire rather than big cannon fire.

Industry's deafness to the need for noise abatement may be described as dollarcusis. It is difficult to "hear" the pitifully weak outcries of an outraged public if every dollar not spent on design for quiet or operations for quiet is seen as a corporate gain. The noise control engineer is either low man on the design totem pole; or kept off the pole altogether. Design for quiet has no tangible sales value.

Economic considerations are not peculiar to the free enterprise system. Attending the Vth International Congress for Noise Abatement in London were several Moscow engineers and physicists working in aviation acoustics. I asked them this question: "In profit-system U.S. the aviation industry justifies not reducing jet noise because it claims such reduction may involve economic penalties in additional operating costs, lower payloads, and so forth. From what little I know of the Soviet jet engines, they may be slightly quieter, but they are no paragons of silence. What is your excuse?"

The one Russian engineer who spoke English grinned sheepishly and replied: "Operating economy."

Product design is a management responsibility. Management evades design for quiet, choosing to design as if human beings had no ears, or homes were located in the middle of silent deserts. Listen to that kitchen blender. Designed to look as beautiful as a space ship, it sounds like the launching of one.

At a safety conference, no less, I asked a manufacturer's representative what was being done to reduce the noise of his line of hand drills and other extremely noisy do-it-yourself tools. At first he didn't understand what I was driving at. I patiently explained about noise.

"Oh, noise. We don't give it a thought. If we did, it would probably be 342nd on our list of priorities."

During a meeting with Detroit automobile executives I raised the question of vehicular noise.

"We have done a great job on the passenger car," replied one of the executives.

"If the driver buys an air-conditioned model and keeps the windows closed," I observed. "That is not the noise I mean. I mean the noise that hits the pedestrian and the public at home."

"Oh, you mean spectator noise. Why, we're not doing anything."

It is unfortunate that noise is associated with large cities, New York especially. Unfortunate, because one finds a dislike of large cities both in industry and in government, not to mention in some conservation circles.

Pollster Lou Harris reported that the American people are aware there is an urban crisis, but couldn't care less. The Washington attitude is said to be, if anyone is dumb enough to live in New York City, let him pay the penalty. Columnist Jack Anderson has explained, "The old men who run Congress come chiefly from rural areas . . . Most of the powerful committee chairmen come from rural towns and do not understand big-city needs." Even city planning commissioners accept stress as a normal part of city living. They permit center-city aviation because aviation progress must not be stopped, and any environmental side-effects are par for city life.

Business executives who live in the quiet suburbs could choose to design for quiet, but they do not regard themselves as their brother's keeper. They see no reason for concern for the quality of urban environments. And they have little respect for the urban environment.

An automobile industry representative, who himself lives in a small town, complained that New York City's noise left him tired and out-of-sorts. When I tried to defend the city, he stopped me. "You've got to admit," he said, "that New York has its unique unpleasant sound."

I took him to a giant construction site. He winced as he walked by the roaring compressors.

"Those noisy engines are not manufactured in New York City."

Next I took him on a tour of East 57th Street, site of some of the best-known specialty shops in the world, and also a main crosstown traffic artery. The poor man winced again, and again, at the horns and the general traffic din.

"It's the automotive industry that's responsible for most of the unpleasant street noises of New York and other cities. Give us quieter buses and trucks, sensible auto horns, and quiet engines for compressors, and we would give you and other visitors a more pleasant environment. The men who dictate our environment live in the suburbs of Detroit."

Dollarcusis is rife in the air conditioning industry. "The engineers," wrote Sheldon Wesson in *Home Furnishings Daily*, "are under great pressure to cut down weight, size and price, with the result that the acoustical properties are largely shoved aside. . . It would mean virtually redesigning all units on the market to make the consumer willing to pay for both reduced noise and cooling comfort." Window units are sold for cooling, not comfort. The president of Lennox Industries acknowledges, "There is no secret to making air conditioning equipment quiet. It simply takes room and money. Design decisions are as much economic as they are scientific."

The eyes have it, and the ears get it.

The goal of industry is not noise reduction, but noise complaint reduction, or as it is known in acoustic circles, "acceptability."

Acceptability does not mean desirability. It means as loud as one can get away with. Acceptability means as noisy as possible with the fewest complaints.

The acceptability criterion punishes large numbers of human beings. Professor Raymond A. Bauer, of the Harvard School of Business Administration, an investigator of the sonic boom and other acoustic phenomena, reported that "the concept of 'tolerable' has a connotation that some may find intolerable. It implies a clear acceptance that the phenomenon involved is unpleasant, but not unpleasant beyond a certain point. In practice this has, in the past, meant the point at which citizen reaction has been intolerable to public officials. . . The National Academy of Engineering report suggests that perhaps one might want to substitute the concept of 'comfort' for that of tolerability. . . . As an old hand at survey research, I can guarantee that if you ask people what level of noise they consider to be 'comfortable' and what level they consider to be 'tolerable,' the latter noise will have a higher level than the former."

One acoustician reports an increase in acceptability by creating a smooth-sounding and continuous artificial background noise level. There is something incongruous in this concept of minimizing some noise by creating constant noise. So little is known about the impact of noise on humans, how can we permit ourselves to be subjected to a lifetime of constant "low-level" noise?

Yet acceptability remains the goal, not a comfortable environment. And since a basic index of acceptability is complaint activity, a great deal of effort is devoted to techniques for reducing complaints. This goal protects the noisemaker from any significant economic burden.

One important technique of this sort is the social survey. People living in a delineated area are interviewed in an attempt to determine their reactions to specific noises in the area.

One of the first major surveys was conducted in the vicinity of London's Heathrow Airport in 1961. A sample was selected from the electoral registers (1,731 people) plus 178 people from a list of those who had complained. The 42-question questionnaire contained items designed to discover what the persons interviewed liked and disliked about their neighborhoods; the effect on them of aircraft, and other noise; their attitudes toward the airport and its importance locally; and their attitudes toward noise in general. Background information such as age, sex, and occupation was also obtained. Questions included:

Does the noise of aircraft bother you very much, moderately, a little, or not at all?

Does the noise of aircraft ever:
  a) wake you up
  b) interfere with listening to TV or radio

    c) make the house vibrate or shake
    d) interfere with conversation
    e) interfere with or disturb any other activity, or bother, annoy, or disturb you in any other way?

Have you ever felt like moving away from this area, and if so why?

Results of such tests are analyzed to show how much noise of a given kind the inhabitants of a given environment can take without serious complaints. Unfortunately, any guidelines developed from such surveys will not be based on a desirable acoustic environment, but on how much people will tolerate; in other words, "acceptability."

The Federal government sponsors community noise studies to collect attitudinal data from airport communities so that it may predict future reactions when existing airports intensify their activities, or when new airports are built. As part of the Federal jet noise alleviation program NASA is accumulating "behavioral psychometric data," which are personality profiles of people who live near airports. One contract was given to two University of North Carolina professors who analyzed residents according to characteristics such as:

    noise sensitivity
    worldly exposure (income, education, air travel experience)
    high anxiety
    anti-aviation
    isolationist (negative attitude to growth and commerce)
    pragmatist
    passivity
    phobia (generalized anxiety about flying and fear from sounds of aviation overhead)
    idealist
    conservative
    imperturbable
    complainer (tends to complain or protest about noise)

Are these two objective academics who are studying a problem of human beings, or—two investigators who started with a
built-in prejudice that all who complain are "different" in some
way?

The main purpose of these studies is to sharpen the tools for
molding a positive attitude toward noise.

The test subjects, incidentally, were exposed to a noise level
of 82 decibels *because it was discovered that at a higher level—
say, 90 decibels—virtually all subjects found the stimuli so annoying that ordinary psychological factors would cease to be part
of the picture.* In other words, whether one has a high or a low
sensitivity—noise is noise.

United States government studies of public reaction to the
sonic boom, supervised by NASA for the FAA, have been
severely criticized. Oklahoma City, site of one of the major
testing programs, is a center of aviation activity, with a direct
stake in aviation development. FAA's Gordon M. Bain foresaw
criticism of what appears to be a loaded sample. In his preface
to the National Opinion Research Center report on the tests, he
wrote: "Another objection to findings in this report may be based
on the nature of the population of Oklahoma City. An estimated
one-third of all residents have ties with aviation, and therefore
might be presumed to possess an ingrained bias pertinent to this
public reaction study. The report found that such connections
did not appear to bias reactions to sonic boom, but there will
inevitably be those who question this conclusion."

Not only is the sample suspect, so is the test itself. The booms
were the less intense ones of the Air Force supersonic bombers,
the shock was not unexpected, the public was carefully informed
of the number of booms per day, it was given assurance of safety
precautions, and finally the public knew that tests would be
stopped, they would not go on for a lifetime.

In tests at Edwards Air Force Base, the subjects were paid by
the hour to knit or read, and then, after a warning signal, told
to record whether the subsonic or the supersonic flyover was

more acceptable. Dr. Lundberg points out that the more appropriate phrasing of the question would have been, "Which noise is *least* acceptable."

When the FAA wanted to arrive at a goal for a lowered aircraft noise level it was aware that from the community response viewpoint the optimum reduction would be a level equal to that of the community's ambient (background noise level). Dismissing this goal as impractical at this time, the FAA decided to opt instead only for a 20 PNdB reduction. (PNdB, or Perceived Noise Decibel, is a calculated decibel that attempts to measure annoyance in terms of "noisiness") They arrived at this number by referring to the work of Bolt, Beranek and Newman which related changes in PNdBs to changes in the attitudes of people in the community. "Levels proposed by the FAA," reported an FAA official, ". . . should be sufficient to cause up to 50 per cent of the people to change from a "vigorous response" to a "no response" category . . . Residual noise will have to be handled by air traffic procedures and compatible land use planning."

Social surveys show a significant but minority number of complaints. Could one reason be that the noise victim has resigned himself to his fate? Such a defeated person, according to one noise survey specialist, "will often tell the investigator that he actually does not usually hear the noise." In other words, a good job of public relations preceding a survey virtually guarantees results pleasing to the noisemaker.

It is ironic that as little as the Federal government knows about the effect of noise on animals, it knows more about porcine and bovine reactions to noise than human reactions. Since swine and cows cannot complain for themselves, the farmer, through his powerful lobbies and well-funded Department of Agriculture, does the complaining for them. And government listens. When farmers worried that jet noise troubled their swine, they had no difficulty getting the Federal government to provide the necessary research. Air Force researchers checked for stress and behavioral changes. They obtained electrocardiograms; they made films of behavioral changes during mating and suckling. But when it comes to jet-stressed human beings we do not perform physiological and behavioral studies; no, we stop at opinion surveys and personality profiles. Are we afraid of what we might find out about the impact of jet noise on human beings living near airports?

One of the more subtle stratagems used by the noisemakers to frustrate noise control has been called The Weighting Game by Jim Botsford of Bethlehem Steel. It stems from the seemingly innocent fact that a small group of noise specialists have become more interested in measuring noise than abating it. To the physical scientist, and the psychologist and sociologist who fail to see the total human being, nothing—including human suffering —exists unless it can be quantified and made to fit into a formula.

Acoustical scientists and technologists embarked on a search for the ultimate measurement of the human "annoyance" response to noise. Esoteric "annoyance" measurements and formulae are devised to try to tell the noisemaker how much noise he can make before the victim yells ouch, how much noise he can make before the victim is moved to active protest.

Central to all schemes for measuring "annoyance" is the decibel.

At one time it was believed that loudness was the determining factor in measuring noise. Most anti-noise ordinances were based on common sense—they prohibited noises that could be described as "unreasonably loud."

With the advent of the decibel meter and its variations, the noise specialist refused to accept the personal complaint of "it's too loud." He began to search for a precise formula, a formula to be based not on individual complaints, but on group judgments. The acousticians preferred to wrestle with statistics instead of noise complainers.

Specialists called *psychoacousticians* started out by trying to quantify the subjective response to noise in terms of loudness. Experiments were devised to try to measure how loud is loud. Juries of listeners were exposed to various levels of noise and asked to rate them as soft or loud, or to compare two sounds as equal or differing in loudness.

As the field of psychoacoustics developed, it was discovered that loudness is only one of many factors that make noise annoying. There followed a proliferation of decibel varieties that continues to this day.

Not content with the pristine decibel, already only an indirect measurement of sound energy, the acoustic power structure, under government contract, embarked on a search for the acoustic holy grail, the ultimate decibel and decibel formula of its limited concept of the human response to noise.

The measurement specialists made a new "discovery": it was not loudness that determined annoyance, but "noisiness." Thus was born the family of perceived noise decibels (PNdBs). Developed originally to apply to aircraft noise, this family is a fertile one; its apparently well-financed promoters come up with one refinement after another. For example, we are told that annoyance varies with the number of noise exposures (such as the number of airplane flyovers), and with the degree of pure tones in a given noise. To account for these variables, the experts have developed a variety of effective perceived noise decibels.

The goal in the use of PNdBs is not a comfortable environment, but one with a minimal number of complaints. The modified PNdBs would make it appear, for example, that less annoyance from fewer aircraft flyovers is the same as no annoyance. Will the use of jumbo jets solve the jet noise problem?

There is now an attempt to add a new decibel-weighting to the readings on the sound level meter, the "D" decibel. Acousticians Robert W. Young of the U.S. Navy and Arnold Peterson of the General Radio Company studied this new "improvement" and concluded: "There is no justification for adding D-weighting to the sound level meter. For simple noise reporting and comparisons the public will benefit, at no loss in precision, if only sound level"A" is employed."

The fragmentation of noise measurement units is what Jim Botsford calls The Weighting Game. Botsford has been sharply critical of this racket in numbers, since he sees such complex measurements as a deterrent to hearing conservation programs in industry. "Methods for estimating the hazard to hearing must be made as simple as possible," he says. After a thorough study of the various schemes for predicting annoyance, speech interference, and hearing loss, this noise control physicist concluded: "The complex methods currently recommended for appraising the effects of noise on people can be replaced by simpler methods utilizing the readings of a standard sound level meter. The small errors introduced by these substitutions are negligible compared to those inherent in the relationship of noise measurements to human response." Botsford pulls no punches in describing how the public is paying, in discomfort and in money, to support The Weighting Game. In a report the magazine *Sound and Vibration* published in October 1969, he wrote:

Human responses to noise can be predicted from sound levels as from any of the more complex noise rating numbers currently recommended. . . . It is highly improbable that the foregoing facts could have escaped discovery under the intense scientific scrutiny that human responses to noise have received. Yet, sound levels are shunned and the development of complicated noise weighting methods continues. This inconsistent and unproductive behavior implies that motivations other than elucidation of human response may spark the investigator's fervor. . . . The activity related to the interactions of people and noise might really be just a game.

The principal players in The Weighting Game are the Researchers, the Consultants, The Noisemakers, and the Public. Each player has his strategy and his winnings except the Public who loses steadily.

Botsford summarizes the Game in a table:

PLAYER	STRATEGY	WINNINGS
Researcher	refines weighting methods endlessly	research contracts, publications, etc.
Noisemaker	lacks information, supports research, waiting for answers	expense of noise abatement postponed
Consultant	helps clients use weightings	fees
Public	wants problem solved	none, pays bill

Referring to this table, he comments: "This program will prove helpful in identifying the players as they are encountered in the field. Masqueraders are quite common in The Weighting Game so, for positive identification of a player, his strategy and winnings must be examined. Often, what appears to be a Researcher will be identified as a Noisemaker by his strategy and his winnings."

No matter how complex, annoyance measurements remain of limited value. Yaffe and Cohen of the Public Health Service state: "While of some value, perceived noise decibels and other annoyance measurements based upon single judgments of the noise stimulus are expected to have only limited usefulness in gauging the complaint potential of a noise. This is due to the many non-acoustical considerations which enter into such judgments."

Herein is a semantic ploy of the first water, because the uninformed are led to believe that what is being measured is the *total* human response to noise. But the subjective reaction of annoyance is *not* the total human response to noise. Conscious annoyance is but a symptom that the human being is disturbed; it is not and cannot be an accurate measure of the extent of that disturbance. (See Chapter 3.)

Loudness, perceived noise, "A" or "D" decibels concentrate on one small aspect of the human response to noise: conscious awareness of irritation. Ignored in the formulae are the effects of noise on sleep, on the emotions, and on the biological processes.

Does it make sense to worry about the nuances of decibels when the receiver is experiencing noise in the 90- and 100-decibel range? Because the prolonged barking of a dog disturbs sleep, we enact ordinances to compel dog owners to keep their pets quiet at night. These anti-barking codes do not specify the size of the dog, or the decibel level of the bark, or even the use of perceived barking dog noise decibels (PBDNdBs). It is accepted that sleep must be protected, and that barking disturbs sleep. Yet when it comes to jet planes or trucks, or air conditioners, all of which can and do disturb sleep, we are asked to wait for the perfect measurement. One of the standing jokes among the noise experts is that the elaborate decibel measurement systems are necessary because the degree of decibel reduction is so minuscule it cannot be detected by simple means!

Enough is known about the physical nature of noise to control it. There is no valid reason for not abating noise first, and measuring it during or afterward.

The methods used to win acceptability for the intense noises of commerce and industry have not worked. Instead, it has become necessary to promote the "final" solution: move the receiver away from the source. "To those who complain of [traffic noise] nuisance," states a leading acoustical consultant, "there is a reasonable reply. Move."

So far government is listening to that old noisemaker's principle: any noise problem, no matter how intense, can be solved by eliminating the people who complain about it.

The aviation industry tells us that economic and technological considerations preclude any significant reduction in jet noise levels, and therefore there is nothing left to do but compel the jet noise victim to move. The euphemism for this "final solution" is *compatible land use.*

The thinking behind this noise control technique is that jet noise is no problem if it is "acceptable" to a majority. The passenger in the plane is not complaining, and other than a little resentment about hearing loss, aviation personnel tend to "accept" jet noise. The only fly in the acceptability ointment is the permanent resident. The final solution now becomes absurdly simple: remove the resident from a zone around the airport where complaints can be expected to be most acute. Then rezone this former residential area for commerce and industry, and, believe it or not, recreation. Presto, the jet noise complaint problem is solved.

Government is being urged to give local communities grants or loans for repurchasing residential property, and to bring pressure to bear on them to rezone property adjacent to airports. The FAA is recommending exploring the possibilities for condemnation or direct purchase followed by resale for other than residential use.

All other things being equal, it may seem logical to rezone around new airports. The question arises, how much urban and near-urban land can be withdrawn from residential development because of airports (and highways)? Here we see "terminus hocus focus" at work. Jet noise is a problem not only at the immediate approach zone, but under other areas such as where stacking occurs. These areas can be several miles from the airport.

It is not a simple matter to condemn property adjacent to airports and then rezone it. There are problems of governmental jurisdiction, the problem of stretching the interpretation of "eminent domain" to include property at a distance from the airport, and so on.

It is not a simple matter to force residents out of their homes because the area has been designated as too loud.

Sidney Goldstein, general counsel for the Port of New York Authority, states the case against zoning as a panacea quite succinctly:

"One must always consider the grave sociological, political, and human problems that would follow in the wake of any large-scale attempt to relocate elsewhere untold numbers of people who now live in noise-affected communities. . . . In the long run it may be even cheaper—and it's certainly more worth while— to put money into the development of quieter aircraft than to pay for the costs of acquiring intrinsically worthless easements of flights in ever-increasing numbers throughout the country. . . . The direct approach obviously is to build quieter planes."

Some idea of what is in store for homeowners near major airports is gleaned from the nationwide plea for help sent out by a Los Angeles homeowners association: "Airport Management is sending a corps of appraisers among the 944 homeowners, going door to door. . . . to persuade them to accept depressed residential prices from the airport. . . . The Los Angeles Planning Commission, urged by the airport authorities, has so far denied [the] right of the individual owners to rezone. . . . The Airport Management's continued attempts to obtain the homes through the appraiser tactic is pursued despite no legal condemnation action. Tragically, most of these 944 average citizens are ignorant of the law, ignorant of their rights, ignorant of commercial values. . . ."

If this situation is being accurately described, we see a new development, whereby airport management can obtain residential property without condemnation. At least condemnation might bring a fairer price. It may come to where homeowners will be forced to be the ones to fight to have their own land condemned.

Many refuse to take this "final solution" seriously. They believe that the billions of dollars in property values would make such a plan economically impossible for already-built-up areas.

But the proponents of compatible land use have an answer: when the area is cleared of residential development, its resale to commerce and industry not only will recoup for the local authority the monies spent on purchasing the condemned property, but will probably earn it a profit. The dispossessed homeowner, who lived for years in a degraded environment, will not participate in this windfall. He will get, like the Los Angeles homeowners, a depreciated market value for residential property.

One of the shocking elements of this "final" solution is the use to which some people are planning to put the rezoned residential property. Mind you, we are talking about property so close to an airport that it is unbearably noisy for human habitation.

What is being recommended is that the residential property be rezoned for commercial, industrial, and *recreational* use. Forgetting the question of what it means to *work* under jets at landing or takeoff, what is it we plan to do to the places to which we retreat for recreation and leisure?

A top FAA official, Oscar Bakke, has stated, "Land in the immediate vicinity of airports must of necessity be restricted to uses that are compatible with normal airport operations. Such compatible uses include parks, recreation areas, automobile parking and light industry."

The solution, it is being suggested, is to reverse the noise victim's home and his recreational areas. Action to implement this program is already underway. Is a miserably noisy park better than no park at all?

Paradoxically, industry organizes and supports its own noise abatement organizations. While these are helping to create an awareness of noise, they are also used to promote the best interests of the noisemaker, or to promote a market for noise-control products. For example, in the 1940s companies manufacturing acoustic tile formed the National Noise Abatement Council. It was the NNAC that consistently rated Memphis, Tennessee, as the quietest city in the United States because it enforced its horn blowing and muffler laws. When the use of acoustic tile became a commonplace, the Acoustical Materials Association withdrew its support and the organization collapsed in 1960.

In 1959 the aviation industry organized the National Aviation Noise Abatement Council (NANAC), composed of the nation's airport operators, pilots, airlines, and manufacturers of engines and airframes. In 1968 the airport operators withdrew from NANAC, denouncing the airlines and aircraft manufacturers for laying "a smokescreen over the problem of jet noise." The Air Line Pilots Association subsequently withdrew financial support because it felt the burden of jet noise reduction was being placed not on quieting the source but on peripheral procedures such as flight operation maneuvers.

The newest industry-oriented group is the National Council on Noise Abatement. Organized in 1968, its advisory committee lists such vested interests as U.S. Steel, International Paper Company, and the Cuna Mutual Insurance Society. Its purpose is to provide a forum for the exchange of information about industrial noise, and noise made by products manufactured in these plants. One of its functions appears to be to serve as a watchdog to alert industry to undesirable government regulations.

Inadvertently or otherwise, industry has succeeded in scuttling what should have been a natural move toward the development of quieter machines and dwelling places.

Whether on earth or in space, the specific province of acoustics, of which noise is one specialty, is the domain of a small group of specialists who literally call the tune we all must listen to. No decibel legislation will be enacted without the direct or tacit approval of these advisors to government and industry.

Scientists themselves can weaken the noise abatement movement. Science and engineering students, according to articles in *The New York Times* and *Physics Today*, are not devoted solely to social values; they are as much or even more interested in personal status as other students, and they often reveal an indifference to the welfare of others. In the course of their training the engineers and physicists who will work in acoustics are taught to look with a jaundiced eye at the complaining public. They cannot be expected to take noise seriously when they are taught, by one of their standard reference books, the *Handbook of Noise Control*, that:"The annoyance produced by some sounds does not mean that they are bad for health, any more than an unsightly billboard is bad for health."

For good measure engineers are further taught that neurotics complain more than others but that "one is not justified in ignoring the likes and dislikes of another because he helps psychiatrists to earn a living." With this kind of indoctrination, which is continued during his professional career, it is not surprising that the noise control worker looks upon protest against noise as the peculiar problem of a peculiar minority; in short, the noise complainer is labeled a kook.

At a meeting of the noise section of the Acoustical Society of America, I asked the assembled noise experts what to advise a couple whose bedroom window was fifteen feet from a neighbor's two window air conditioner units operating day and night, year-round. This couple's physician had recommended sedation, and I thought these experts might have a more practical answer. They did.

"Tell 'em to buy an air conditioner for themselves."

I later received a letter from one of the more understanding members of that audience who apologized for the cynical behavior of his colleagues, to whom this illustration of human suffering had been a big joke.

Civilian noise abatement does not appeal to many scientists, especially the physical scientists. Physical scientists—especially physicists—appear to dominate the scientific establishment. Next come chemists, engineers, and mathematicians. Conspicuous by their absence from the upper echelons of the science complex are men from the behavioral sciences: anthropology, ecology, sociology, psychology, political science.

In practice the top scientists of government and private sectors are one family, with members of the President's Scientific Advisory Committee often holding interlocking positions with the National Academy of Science (NAS) and the newer National Academy of Engineering (NAE). Any President of the United States is both captor and captive of this scientific establishment. Though he decides the goals, the scientists, through their influence and "expert" opinions, mold his decisions. Dissenters from orthodox scientific or Federal policies are kept out.

It is difficult to imagine that the research priorities of the nation have not been influenced by this closely knit complex.

Therefore, as long as Science tells the public, and Congress, that everyday noise is a mere nuisance we must put up with, we will not get the research we need to arouse us to action, and we will not get the legislation that will be needed.

Though there is no formal *acoustic* establishment, the small size of the acoustic world, the control of policy by a few academic and private consultants, the allocation of government contracts, all tend to create the semblance of an "in" group, or establishment. The main pipeline for noise knowledge between the private and government sectors is the National Research Council Committee on Hearing, Bioacoustics and Biomechanics (formerly the Armed Services Committee . . .), referred to as CHABA.

Why CHABA has had little, if anything to offer the public is indicated by its sponsors and its function. The sponsors are the Department of Defense, the Federal Aviation Administration, and the National Aeronautics and Space Administration. The Departments of Health, Education and Welfare and of Housing and Urban Development are affiliated with CHABA, but not as sponsoring members. Composed of acoustic and noise control experts, CHABA "gives direction and advice toward the solution of acoustic problems submitted by [its] sponsoring agencies." In other words, CHABA serves the military and space, not the civilian earth agencies. There are some who would like to see CHABA pay more attention to the civilian noise problem, but without a radical restructuring it is unlikely CHABA would have its heart in the abatement of everyday noise.

In 1967 I had the opportunity of observing for myself at least one example of how some scientists inadvertently help to perpetuate the noisy status quo. The event was a "Seminar for Science Writers on Noise Pollution" sponsored by the American Institute of Physics. Those in attendance were members of the National Association of Science Writers. This is what they were told about noise and health by the medical speaker, a past officer of CHABA:

On the sonic boom: "Not in the ball park as to injury. Pounds per square inch not significant enough when compared with that of artillery pressures. Sonic boom won't hurt you. Maybe you'll get hit by a piece of flying glass, but not if you jump fast enough."

Bodily harm: "There is hazardous noise exposure that causes hearing loss. But this type of injurious effect has little to do with noise pollution and is of no concern to the community. It is an industry problem and industry is solving it."

Noise pollution: "Noise pollution is the community noise problem—it is a problem of intrusion, of speech interference, and annoyance. There is inadequate information on the significance of speech interference and sleep disturbance. Annoyance is psychological, all in the mind."

Effect on body chemistry; endocrine glands: "That's animal research."

One writer asked if the doctor wasn't concerned because of the additional stresses to which human beings were now being subjected, plus the new ones around the corner. He answered that the human being, as proven by history, has tremendous capabilities for adapting, and that he had every confidence it would adapt to noise stress.

This credo, that the human being can and must adapt to the machine, and not the reverse, helps maintain a noisy world.

Lack of progress in understanding the complex human response to noise is due, in part, to the fact that hearing-oriented specialists dominate the field. These men have consistently downgraded the extra-auditory impact of noise. They take a dim view of those who claim that everyday noise is more serious than a mere nuisance. Some become emotional and let fly at any who dare to challenge their "expert" opinions. At the National Conference on Noise as a Public Health Hazard, one otologist presented a paper covering questions frequently asked about the effects of noise. A brief excerpt illustrates how this "dispassionate" scientist reacts to critics of noise:

> *Finally, is it true that we are continually surrounded by ultrasound —sound too high in frequency to be heard—and so as a result we are being deafened and maddened by this sound we cannot even hear, as some fanatics claim?* I trust the answer to this question is implicit in the way the question was phrased.

If these men are so secure in their belief that noise is not a serious problem, except as they define it, why do they get so upset at their critics?

I had occasion to witness a histrionic display of intolerance of noise critics, at an institute for occupational hearing loss operated for industrial hygienists and factory medical directors. One of the speakers was a Fellow of several scientific and professional societies and a consultant on toxicology, air pollution, water pollution, noise, and environmental health. As part of his lecture he had repeated the traditional doctrine that the only damage from noise was hearing loss, as defined. He was upset because the public was told there may be other forms of harm. To illustrate how the public was being given distorted information, he held up a copy of a popular household magazine sold in food markets. He made it very clear this was *not* a scientific magazine. He became more and more emotional as he read excerpts from the article that suggested noise was a health hazard, that kitchens were unduly noisy, and that the inner ear was like a snail. This anatomical description was as much as he could take, and with a dramatic gesture he ripped out the three pages of the offending article and said: "Now this magazine is fit to come into my home."

As calmly as possible I asked him this carefully-worded question: "Is it your contention that, other than hearing loss from specific exposures, noise has no significant non-auditory health effects?"

He gasped at this unexpected question, and while he fumbled for a reply, the institute's medical director rephrased my question.

"Baron wants to know if it isn't true that noise gives you heart attacks, and ulcers, causes divorce. . . ."

Noise is closely linked to the same sickness that keeps us from solving the human problems of housing, education, civil rights, unemployment, and health care, while at the same time solving the difficult and expensive problems of faster air transportation, a national highway system, sophisticated weaponry, and a scheduled route to the moon.

Undoubtedly influenced by the carefully nurtured idea that noise is a mere nuisance, municipal government typically meets the demand for noise abatement with ignorance, indifference, or arrogance. There have been no policy positions that the human being has the right to sleep, keep from straining his vocal chords, be free from unnecessary distraction. There are no effective ordinances, administrative rulings, guidelines, or even an impartial abatement advisory service.

When a strict law is passed, it is to curb the politically impotent, like ice cream vendors.

It is a rare event for effective anti-noise legislation to be introduced into a city council, even rarer for it to become law, and rarely has it happened in America that an anti-noise law is both meaningful and commonly enforced.

Pet animals are not allowed on the streets without a leash, but undomesticated noisemakers can operate freely on the ground and in the sky. The jackhammer and the rock drill should never have been permitted inside the city limits without a promise of eventual good behavior. The city could, as we will see, move to cut down many of the excessive noises that have become characteristic of larger population centers. It could lobby in Washington to oppose environment-destroying highways and deny land for noisy airports.

Only one municipality, New York City, has so much as an official noise abatement function—so far equipped with responsibility but no authority—and only one other, Honolulu, is contemplating following suit. In between these two cities sit the thousands of indifferent governments, smug in the knowledge that most people believe you can't fight City Hall.

One would think it impossible for legislators who ignore noise abatement not to alienate constituents. But the legislator can afford to maintain the noisy status quo, because industry and the scientists back him up with their interpretation of noise control. Legislators provide the money for the very research that the noisemaker is able to cite in defense of today's noise. As we have seen, industry-oriented government actually helps originate and disseminate the propaganda that protects noisemaking by industry. In protecting each other's self-interest, industry and government are involved in a system that escalates the noise output. On the surface it is hard to understand why former Congressman Kupferman's bill calling for an office of noise control in HEW could not get out of committee. It set no standards, and in the best tradition of conservative politics, it gave most of the first year's $3 million budget back to the states and the cities. Could it be that the pro-industry agencies would not like to see a strong, centralized noise abatement function, especially in HEW?

We tend to forget that the day-to-day operation of government, on all levels, is conducted by administrative agencies. Their officials appear content to be misinformed by the noisemaker, especially if his actions mean a larger empire for a given agency. When the acting commissioner of New York's Department of Marine and Aviation was asked about the impact of a giant STOLport on that city's environment, he replied that his responsibility was to foster aviation, and what happened to the environment was somebody else's problem.

There have been illusory exceptions to government callousness. The 1956 noise study situation looked promising when Mayor Wagner initiated the Committee for a Quiet City. After four years of study it reported that noise was so dangerous it could even be a killer. Alarmed by its own conclusions, its funds exhausted, it ended its life with a vigorous campaign against horn honking.

As the years went on, the Federal government heard of noise. While the subway project continued to rattle my windows, the President's Scientific Advisory Committee received a report from a special Environmental Pollution Panel. "The public should come to recognize individual rights to quality of living, as expressed by the absence of pollution, as it has come to recognize the right to education, to economic advance, and to public recreation." Marvelous. The Magna Charta for noise abatement. But there was only one specific recommendation for noise abatement, that "the Federal government encourage the development and adoption of codes governing insulation in apartment buildings."

This lone recommendation for quiet appeared in 1965. As of 1970—nothing.

There is something grotesque about the fact that we spend ten times more on chewing gum than on mental health research, and the fact that the State of New York's Department of Mental Hygiene could not be authorized $75,000 to study the effects of jet noise on people living near airports. Even research on the hearing problems of children goes begging while scientists in Hawaii are testing tuna for their hearing capabilities.

Several years ago Representative Benjamin S. Rosenthal rebutted the head of the FAA, who had cited to a Congressional subcommittee statistics that gave the impression substantial sums were being spent on engine research: " . . . The fact Mr. Halaby said we are spending a million and a half dollars for engine research is just a drop in the bucket. Sir, I voted for a $10-million aquarium in the District of Columbia. I have no regrets about it. I think it is a good thing. We did that partially so that fish could have a quiet place to spawn. I think for the perpetuation of the race as I know it, at least in my district* they are entitled to the same thing as the fish—$10 million for the fish and $1.5 million for my people—there is no comparison."

More than twice as much money—$250,000 a year—is spent annually on research on Bang's Disease in cattle than on the Public Health Service budget for community and industrial noise control. It is hard to believe that the most powerful nation in the world, the nation with the technological "most," has a PHS staff of five to handle the occupational noise problems of perhaps 30 million or more workers, plus servicing the cities and the states for community noise problems.

Such Federal activity as there is focuses mainly on the jet noise problem. In 1968 Congress authorized the FAA to certificate aircraft for noise levels and to set criteria for sonic booms. Called the cat and the canary bill by the insiders, in fifteen years or so it may bring into production new aircraft of somewhat quieter levels.

There may be promise in the new Department of Transportation Noise Abatement Office, which under Colonel Charles Fos-

*The 8th, Queens, New York.

ter seems to be serious about tackling a wide spectrum of noise sources, not alone aircraft. Foster set up the first national conference on evaluating transportation noise. He is concerned with motor vehicle noise, and welcomes the input from the concerned citizen.

Another healthy development is the opening of government-sponsored noise control meetings to the public. The presence of the concerned citizen is a reminder that the end product of noise abatement is the human being, and not measurement or machines. If he has done his homework, he can challenge many assumptions and statements that have so far been accepted as gospel. As one example, at a Department of Transportation symposium on evaluating criteria for transportation noise, a spokesman for the automotive industry gave the impression that it was busy tackling the problem of effective noise standards. I asked this simple question:

"The automotive industry once told the City of New York it was setting up a committee to work on standards for the auto horn. That was in 1930. It is now 1969. Has the committee been formed and has it submitted its report?"

You know the stunned answer.

Noise-abatement crusading has its delicious moments, and that was one of them.

PART IV

Design for Quiet

CHAPTER EIGHT

Potential For Control

Broadway director and drama critic Harold Clurman and I were walking along one of Manhattan's lovelier streets one balmy spring day. A truck barreled by. He winced, and we had to stop conversing. As we progressed, a jackhammer suddenly opened up at a street repair site. He winced again, much disturbed by these noises, but he failed to make any comment.

"Doesn't this noise upset you?" I asked, when I could.

"Upset me! That's putting it mildly. Have you ever tried to direct a show with heavy truck traffic outside the rehearsal hall, not to mention the sirens and the horns? Can you imagine putting together a play review while living next to a construction site? But what can I do? Noise is one of the curses of civilization."

"Would you believe trucks could be designed with less noise, and that jackhammers are made with built-in mufflers?"

"Stop pulling my leg," he replied. "You've been reading too much science fiction."

Noisy equipment is a sign of imperfect design. At the same time that man's inventiveness has enabled him to produce the noisiest epoch in his history, it has also given him tools for eliminating or minimizing all that noise. So refined is the application of these tools, noise control experts have designed a systems approach to any given noise problem. Its formula is "source/transmission-path/receiver."

Translated into action, this formula means that to solve a noise problem the first step is to find a way to eliminate noise at its source. If not, block the sound waves after they are generated. Or, finally, find a way to separate the receiver's ear and the acoustic energy.

The science and technology of noise control are quite sophisticated. Equipment can be designed to meet goals for preventing hearing loss, for permitting speech communication, for minimizing "annoyance." The design engineer has available a limited number of guidelines ranging from voluntary codes adopted by an entire industry to purchase specifications and—rarely—legislation.

Some guidelines set limits for the allowable noise to be emitted by a given machine, others, for the amount of noise allowed at the receiver's ears. Most available guidelines or standards specify what instruments are to be used to measure the noise, and how these measurements are to be taken. The basic measuring instrument is the sound level meter. This device—which comes in all sizes, including portable, hand-held models—makes possible the comparison of various sound intensities ranging from the decibel reading in a bedroom at night to the sound intensity of a passing truck or jet. Sound level meters are in use throughout the world. One manufacturer prints instruction sheets in sixteen languages, including French, Russian, Norwegian, German, Finnish, Japanese, and Chinese.

There are also instruments for analyzing the decibel level of sounds at various frequencies. With these analyzers it is possible to tell how much of the sound energy is in the low pitch, middle pitch, or high pitch range. They can analyze the acoustic energy in hisses, swishes, sizzles, rattles, and buzzes, and can be used for the rating of product noises, the measurement of noises proscribed by local ordinances, and the designing of auditoria. It should be noted that though they are commonly referred to as noise meters, the sound level meter and the analyzer are, more correctly, means of measuring the two physical qualities of sound—intensity and frequency; they do not measure human response to noise.

For acoustical research and design applications, technology has provided an incredible array of more sophisticated measuring and analyzing instruments based on decibel measurements. There are impact analyzers, to measure impulsive noises too brief to give a reading on the dial of the regular sound level meter. There are oscilloscopes, by means of which sound can be observed and measured visually. There are tape machines that can record noise on location for subsequent analysis in acoustic laboratories. As you listen to your noisy appliances, think of the noise level meter available for factory production lines to assess the noise and vibration output of each item.

The most effective and possibly the least expensive method of noise abatement (as far as society is concerned) is to design machines that generate and radiate little noise. Engineers can be trained to determine if a given noise can be reduced at its source. Machine noise is not "natural." According to one consulting engineer, "Noise is a form of pollution that is not necessarily inherent in the design of larger, more powerful systems and equipment. It is not necessary for design engineers to accept increased noise and vibration as an unavoidable accompaniment to the power, capacity, and efficiency of industrial machinery."

Given the motivation, engineers can select silent operating levels, can specify low tolerances for moving surfaces, can call for the use of bearings with relatively few imperfections. (It is said that bearings of the future will be made in outer space, with the result that each bearing will come out perfect.) Gears can be designed to make less noise, and in some cases they can be fabricated of nylon or other plastic instead of noisier metal.

Engineers can check thin metal housings for vibration, and rotating machinery for imbalance. They can select a type of metal that will not vibrate as readily as another.

With or without guidelines, the motivated engineer can measure the decibels as a diagnostic means of tracing machine parts that are responsible for unwanted or unnecessary sound. For example, in precision design, an air conditioner or lawn mower could be isolated in an anechoic room—a room so quiet that one begins to hear the internal sounds of his own body—in order to determine the total sound power level. The design engineer can isolate tones, obtaining a picture of how the noise energy is distributed, from rumble to high squeal. Moving parts making unwanted sounds can be identified.

One of the most dramatic examples of effective silencing—the car muffler—was developed before there was a science and technology of decibels, even before the invention of the sound level meter. The automobile industry had to develop effective muffling to keep from frightening horses on the roads. Unfortunately, we do not insist that new noise-suppression methods be developed to keep from frightening humans.

Noisy machines can be partially or completely enclosed in barriers. At Baden-Baden a dramatic reduction of noise was achieved by placing what looked like an open-ended privy around a jackhammer and an air compressor. The open end, which faced away from the public, provided light and ventilation, while sound-absorbent lining made life a little more bearable for the operator.

In this country, partial or full enclosures are employed in factories to protect machine operators from noise produced by very noisy automatic screw machines and jolt-squeeze hammers. (Similar enclosures are available for electric typewriters and calculating machines.) Several companies make standardized soundproof panels that are fitted together to shield noise-sensitive areas in factories. This principle could be adapted to enclose suburban electrical generating stations, noisy turbine generators, and other sources of noxious noise.

It is possible to stop the transmission of noise through attached structures by breaking the acoustic path through walls and floors. With vibration isolators, springs, pads, or rubber mounts in use, apartment dwellers need not suffer from noises radiated from elevator or central air conditioning operations. Ford, Bethlehem Steel, and other industrial giants reduce the noise of operating equipment to safe levels by placing shock and vibration mounts under machines.

Window air conditioners operate less noisily if properly mounted: that is, isolated from the window structure. Resilient gasketing keeps the vibrations of rotating parts from being transmitted to the windows, and into the walls, floors, and ceilings. Even the tiny motors used to aerate fish tanks can create quite a hum. If placed on a foam rubber or other resilient base, however, their noise-making is reduced.

Most of the literature of noise control quickly glosses over the most fundamental approach: source substitution. Noisy equipment and processes can be replaced with quieter substitutes. Bolting and welding are quieter ways of putting up a building than riveting. The banging of punch presses can be eliminated by substituting hydraulic pressure to shape the metal.

Electric motors can be substituted for noisy internal combustion engines. Electric vehicles, in use in England, not only make but little noise, they have no exhaust fumes. Small electric lorries, tested at normal town speeds, were much quieter at a distance of 7 meters than diesel and gasoline counterparts:

diesel	81 dB(A)
petrol	80 dB(A)
electric	60 dB(A)

Diesel and gasoline vehicles are even noisier when shifting gears or accelerating.

Another quieter substitute for the internal combustion engine is the gas turbine engine, and turbine-operated buses are undergoing operating tests. Air compressors operated by propane gas engines are strikingly quiet. Fuel cells and steam engines provide quiet power without air pollution.

Other examples of quiet by means of substitution are the use of plastic or paper sacks instead of metal garbage cans, nylon rollers instead of metal. The list of quiet substitutes for clangers and bangers is quite long.

Being a practical people, we want to know how much it will cost to make things that will operate with less noise. Though the impression has been created that quieter design and excessive costs go hand in hand, there is no universal law that says this is so. A metal garbage can without clang might cost $1.50 more than standard cans, but given volume and improved design the price differential would become meaningless. The quieter, less polluting chassis for the first 400 garbage trucks ordered by the City of New York cost less than $100 extra. The ten dramatically quiet garbage trucks subsequently ordered by New York cost $17,000 each, as against $15,000 for the noisy models. But these are experimental units, and should go down in price as they are produced in volume.

An 85-pound silenced jackhammer imported into the United States for public demonstration by CQC cost $175 *less* than its unmuffled American counterpart. Comparing unmuffled and muffled imports showed an increase of but $60, or 11.6 per cent. The first large-size (900 cfm) silenced air compressor cost 25 per cent more, but this increase of $9,300 must be placed in perspective: a portable air compressor may operate for five years before requiring extensive repairs. The projects on which these machines are used may cost in the millions of dollars. Any marginal addition to the cost for silencing is not significant.

As for appliances, engineering professor Howard Kingsbury smeared all panel surfaces of an automatic washer and undercounter diswasher with a fibered automotive undercoat and glued to this a glass fiber blanket. Resilient pads were placed around the dishwasher to separate it from the floor and counter structure. The result was a much quieter appliance; the isolating cost pennies on a do-it-yourself basis, and if done commercially by the manufacturer it might add not more than between $2 and $5 to the cost.

The Federal Council for Science and Technology supports the conclusion implicit in Professor Kingsbury's experience: "It is possible that quiet devices and appliances could be built at the same and perhaps even less cost than their noisy counterparts by the use of appropriate design."

Quieter dishwashers and other appliances, because of improved design and less vibration, last longer and require less maintenance expense. Quieter appliances built into dwellings add little to construction costs. A quiet siphon-jet toilet may cost only $5 more than an ordinary noisy one. Canvas connecting sleeves to prevent furnace rattle and rumble from being transmitted through the house via the ductwork may add but $12. Noiseless nylon rollers in the overhead garage doors may cost only $5 more than the noisy metal ones.

Adequate statistics on the cost of sound-conditioning dwellings are not readily available. One reads of additional costs ranging from 2 percent to 10 percent. Care must be taken to ask, per cent of what? The basic construction cost? Or, the much greater total cost which includes financing and other non-construction costs?

Some builders and the FHA regard improved design as a plus factor. Referring to the problems of noisy dwellings, the magazine *Buildings* stated: "Fortunately there are solutions which can be obtained with a small investment in vibration and noise control and which will result in a high degree of occupancy and tenant satisfaction."

The FHA reports that noise control, if considered early in the planning stages, not only can be surprisingly inexpensive, but can be designed to yield other benefits as well, such as thermal insulation.

Speaking of costs, never a peep is heard about the astronomical costs of noise control in defense and space projects. Who tells the Department of Defense that its noise control programs are too costly, or that the noise that makes a submarine audible to the enemy is the price of progress?

The tyranny of noise could be ended if society *asked* that noise emissions be reduced and that structures be noise-insulated. The armed services and the defense-related space program ask, and receive, such noise control from the manufacturers of materials they use. Budget priorities have made it possible for man to know more about noise in space, in space capsules, and under the seas than he does about noise in his cities.

With the almighty power of the contract, the military have called upon industry to subdue the most awesome of noise sources, and to perform prodigious feats of combining power and propulsion with quiet. These non-public sectors also build themselves offices and living quarters that are oases of quiet in the midst of jet whine and rocket blast associated with the space program and military bases.

Though the first municipal office of noise control, New York City's, was not announced until 1969, the Air Research and Development Command recognized the growing requirement for research data on noise and its control as early as 1952. In that year it created the Office of Coordinator of Noise and Vibration Control. In 1954, faced with many complaints from communities near air bases, the Air Force sponsored the first major Federal government study on community reaction to noise. (Unfortunately for the public, this and subsequent studies revealed that community responses to aircraft noise "are influenced by many variables.")

Since 1953 the Air Force has been designing installations in and around air bases to meet noise-control criteria. In 1957, these criteria were improved and published for the guidance of base commanders. In 1954 the Air Force initiated a program to study missile noise, its generation, propagation, effects, and control.

To cope with noise problems in outer space and in the skies, the Air Force in 1957 opened a $1.3 million Bioacoustics Research Facility for studying the effects of high-intensity noise on man. This facility has specialized noise exposure rooms, audiometric rooms, medical observation rooms. It is the only laboratory of its type in the country, if not in the world. When first opened, it was staffed with thirty scientists and engineers. Ten years later—at a cost of $12.4 million—the Air Force opened its Sonic Fatigue Facility to investigate the effects of noise on materials. This facility was staffed with fifty scientists and engineers.

By 1960 Congress could be told that the Air Force was attacking the noise problem with a systems approach, "to insure control of human exposure to acoustic energy and vibration, to assure levels of acoustic energy that would be acceptable to humans in a normal working or living environment, to prevent damage to structures by controlling acoustic energy levels, and to provide or develop general noise criteria for aircraft and missiles upon which to base airbase and missile site planning."

The U.S. Navy has had a shipboard noise problem for many years, most particularly on aircraft carriers. In 1952 the Navy's Bureau of Medicine and Surgery started its first significant research approach when it measured the noise levels on the flight deck. Noise intensities frequently reached more than 130 decibels. As a result of this research the Navy contracted with the Psychoacoustic Laboratory at Harvard University for additional noise studies. During 1954 and 1955 great strides were made in the development of earplugs and other ear protection devices. In 1960 the Navy issued contracts to two industrial concerns for research and development of an advanced-type portable ground suppressor that muffled the noises generated by the jet engine and its exhaust.

Most of the Navy's current research has gone underseas, where it is expected some of the key battles of the future will be fought. While few cities have as much as a sound level meter, the Navy's acoustic research facilities range from two-man submarines to the 354-foot SPAR (Seagoing Platform for Acoustics Research). SPAR is used to study underwater sound transmission and propagation, and can make highly precise noise measurements at depths of 300 feet. This is all the more interesting because on dry land, civilian noise experts cannot agree on a practical, enforceable method of accurately measuring highway motor vehicle noise at 50 feet!

There have been no noise-abatement developments in civilian hardware comparable in sophistication—or cost—with the new breed of submarines that silently ply the seas. These technological marvels run by powerful motors are ventilated and cooled by motor-driven devices; they contain generators, compressor, fans —in short, almost every type of mechanical and electrical noise source. But if they operate noisily their price of progress will be death. To elude detection by the electronic ears of an enemy, these subs' diesel engines are enclosed in acoustic enclosures; their special engines are designed to meet "tuned" frequencies —that is, not to exceed more than the prescribed number of decibels in each of specified octave bands.

With the help of a $150 million authorization from Congress, the Navy works on an *improved* "quiet" submarine, which they hope will be 30 per cent quieter than the current model. Elaborate design changes include the substitution of electric-driven propulsion for current diesel systems. A slow speed of 25 knots will further reduce noise emissions, and bearings, an important source of noise, will be given special attention.

The U.S. Army has been conducting a variety of researches, including developing a quiet airplane. Military editor Hanson Baldwin reported in *The New York Times* (October 17, 1967): "The Army of tomorrow will reconnoiter the battlefield with silent aircraft. . . . The study of silent planes to replace noisy helicopters for surveillance behind enemy lines or over battlefields includes tests of a new Lockheed QT-2 . . . [that] flies so quietly . . . it is difficult to hear. Modified versions of the Grumman OV-1 Army observation plane are also being tested."

Once preoccupied with aviation noise, NASA by 1960 had reoriented its noise research towards investigating the noise problem of manned space flight and sonic boom. During space launchings, astronauts must be, and are, shielded from noise intensities of more than 175 decibels, and from accompanying low-frequency energy that could cause harmful vibrations within their bodies.

Even attack missiles are protected. When it was discovered that the intense noise generated by the launching of ICBMs from concrete underground silos was damaging the "skin" of the missile and its delicate instruments, a method was found to reduce exposure by lining the silos with sound-absorbent material.

Civil Defense demands and gets more acoustic expertise than peacetime functions. When the Civil Defense people wanted to know how well sound in the form of sirens and the spoken word traveled down city streets, money was found for a thorough study under private contract. How much money does your community have for measuring fire engine sirens and outdoor speech communication?

Not until 1963 did the Public Health Service publish a detailed analysis of hospital noise and its control, covering all potential noise sources from site selection to bedpans. An analogous guide was published three years earlier by the British Standards Institution.

Noise control is no secret to hotel and motel operators. In

1955 a University of Michigan professor compiled a detailed program of motel sound control. Owners were told to try to avoid noisy sites, to angle buildings and set them back from highways, and to try to flank them with other buildings.

It was also pointed out that management could protect guests by controlling certain outdoor operations: noisy power mowers should not be run during hours of sleep, and room cleaning should not be scheduled for too early in the morning. Even seemingly small touches were suggested: using wooden wall racks on sound-resistant walls (instead of metal hangers on resonant doors), sound-deadening metal rods by wrapping them with tape or a plastic covering, adjusting phone bells or buzzers to limit the sound, and installing silent door closers and volume controls in radio and TV sets. It was even suggested that windows be checked for rattle.

To obtain and disseminate its noise control know-how, private industry sponsors factory noise control research, industrial noise symposia, and hearing-conservation programs. It supports the work of professional societies responsible for developing standards. On its payrolls are acoustical engineers and medical specialists in industrial hearing loss.

Enlightened management knows the danger signs for hearing loss and accidents: if conversation at arm's length is impossible in the plant; if warning signals are inaudible; if telephone use is made difficult because of noise. Design goals for factory machinery are usually concerned with reducing the noise level to as close as possible to 85 decibels in the critical speech frequencies (500, 1,000, and 2,000 cps.). Given the noise emission of a particular machine or process, management can take steps to regulate the amount of time the worker is exposed to dangerous noise, or urge him to use ear protectors.

Bethlehem Steel, DuPont, Western Electric, and Ford are among the big companies that undertake internal noise control and hearing-conservation programs. General Motors' new foundry at Defiance, Ohio, was designed to incorporate current concepts in noise control. The interior of all outside walls is covered with acoustical paneling four inches thick. Individual high-noise-level operations inside the buildings are housed in sound-barrier construction.

Industrial hearing-conservation programs include an analysis of noise exposure *and* the measurement of the employees' hearing acuity. An ideal plant hearing conservation committee is comprised of the plant manager, the company physician, the industrial relations manager, labor relations supervisor, workmen's compensation representative, plant engineer, and manufacturing engineer.

Noise-conscious industry does not expect that it will be able to buy every noise-control product it needs "off the shelf." Many noise controls must be engineered within the plant or especially designed by vendors.

Not only is some industry willing to custom-build when necessary, it is willing to experiment. It recognizes that the consideration of noise in design is, as Jim Botsford puts it, "in its infancy —there are few established guidelines to follow. Each noise problem is unique. Many noise problems can be solved from an evaluation of the environment, by proper use of available criteria or guidelines, and by use of available information on noise control. The job does not end with the design of the noise control measures. Their performance must be checked after installation and modifications made if needed because noise control in industry is still based partially on trial and error."

What a contrast to the attitude of local bureaucrats who turn a deaf ear to pleas for noise control, on the grounds that the equipment to implement it is not readily available on the market, and do not seem to be imaginative enough to think in terms of having the needed equipment devised.

Nothing representing industrial awareness and use of noise control permeates the public sector of American life. Why should it? Industry expects a payoff in fewer claims for hearing loss and accidents, more productivity, and public acceptance of the plant's presence and activities. Its noise control program is further testimony to a double standard: noise control for the private (and military) sector, and just plain noise for the public. Yet with motivation, the builder or maker of things could provide convenience and speed to the public, without the excessive noise.

Though Europeans are subjected to many of the same disturbing noises of commerce and traffic that affect Americans, there is a basic difference: an attitude that men should be protected from excessive noise. Consequently, many Europeans benefit from advances in everyday noise control.

Many responsible citizens in Europe have organized against noise. National organizations belong to the International Association Against Noise, or AICB. Incorporated as an international organization since 1959, AICB convenes a congress on noise abatement every two years, providing a much-needed forum for the exchange of information.

Many areas of government, on national and local levels, show responsiveness to the noise problem. There is more of a commitment to abate, as evidenced by the laws, personnel to enforce the laws, and acoustic laboratories to back up enforcement and pave the way for improvements.

Zurich (population 600,000) has two agencies for noise control: public health, and the police. A half-day spent with the Zurich noise control police in 1966 was quite a revelation, after experiencing the abysmal ignorance and indifference of New York City's government.

The Zurich Police Office of Noise Control consists of a shared-time commissioner and four fulltime sergeants. Each sergeant is required to have ten years of experience as a patrolman, plus one year of noise abatement study at the *hochschulle*. He must keep up to date on noise abatement developments. Facilities include an assortment of decibel-measuring instruments. One room of the office contains an exhibit of noise-control products, including jackhammer mufflers and building materials that keep out sound. This "library" is visited by noisemakers who want to employ noise abatement methods, and by anti-noise law violators.

An American policeman, hearing a motor vehicle with an obviously noisy muffler, can issue a summons. However, if the operator chooses to plead not guilty, the policeman must spend a day in court and satisfy the judge that the vehicle in question was creating "unreasonably loud" noises. This time-consuming and subjective enforcement procedure discourages strict enforcement.

Contrast this cumbersome and lengthy procedure with that in Switzerland (or Germany) where if a policeman issues a citation for a noisy vehicle, the operator(or owner) is required to take the vehicle to a testing station immediately, and cannot drive it again until it is certified as suitably quiet. In Zurich, the police keep the operator's license until the repairs are completed.

The German Federal government has been able to regulate traffic noise for decades because decibel standards have been set for the whole spectrum of motor vehicles, including motor bikes. An operator's license is issued only if there is no violation of these standards. It is also a general philosophy of both German and Swiss motor vehicle laws that the permitted limits will be lowered step by step as technical advances permit.

In addition to muffler control, German and Swiss regulations cover vehicle operations. Drivers must not coast or start out in other than first; unnecessary slamming of car doors, trunks, and hoods is prohibited, as are unnecessary idling and starting of motor bikes in courtyards, gateways, or passages of apartment houses, and slamming of garage doors. In France, automobile radios may be turned on only while the car is moving.

In spite of decibel standards and strict enforcement, traffic noise in Europe remains disturbing. One European acoustic expert, who has been responsible for setting limits, explains:

"Yes, our traffic is noisy. We are fighting to maintain a level. Each year there are more vehicles on the road, therefore more noise. We try to lower the permitted levels to at least prevent an increase in the over-all noise generated. Can you imagine what it would be like without any standards? "

It is especially interesting that the Zurich police claim they are stricter than the health department inspectors who, they say, tend to adhere too strictly to decibels. The police depend on an initial human-subjective reaction. Measurements follow, not precede, listening. "A policeman must use his head and his heart to be a good noise policeman," one of them told me. Amen.

The Swiss government has an acoustic testing facility larger and more complete than any non-military facility in the United States. The Netherlands, population 12,660,000, has a Sound Division in its Research Institute for Public Health Engineering. We do not even have a research facility for public health engineering.

The British government has facilities elaborate enough to develop standards and sound insulation data for dwellings, experiment with soundproofing units for homes near airports, research quieter paving-breakers, and conduct noise surveys.

It was my privilege to be the guest of Dr. R.J. Stephenson, Assistant to the Scientific Advisor for the Greater London Council. He showed me GLC's acoustic laboratory facilities and mobile noise testing laboratory. This *local* government lab has researched the acoustic profile of tall buildings, the noise contour of urban motorways, techniques for shielding residential sites from roadways, techniques for soundproofing windows and providing sound-trapped ventilation, scales for evaluating the relationship between different types of windows and aircraft noise intrusion, studies of the impact of helicopter noise on the urban environment. Also investigated was the effect of traffic vibration on historic buildings, particularly when new roads are being planned.

Where can the American public go for similar information?

The only way we learn about the impact of traffic noise and vibration and construction blasting is when it cracks a water main and floods the neighborhood.

European health departments, both local and national, are involved with noise abatement. This does not mean they have all of the needed power to curb the serious noisemakers, but they recognize the issue, they press for constructive legislation, they encourage public and professional debate. They have laboratory facilities. In the Netherlands, noise standards for dwellings are developed by a public health engineering facility. Local health authorities in England take an active role in reducing construction noise. They cooperate with the Noise Abatement Society in educational campaigns, in following up noise complaints; they sponsor demonstrations of quieter products; they present experience papers at noise abatement conferences.

In Germany, the Ministry of Health believes both Federal and local governments in all social conscience have a duty to fight intolerable noise situations. It recognizes that legal commands and prohibitions are necessary to restrain human thoughtlessness and negligence. It also recognizes that without laws the development and use of noise control knowledge will remain largely unrealizable.

Under administrative law the German police, too, are involved in noise control. Here is one of their guidelines:

"The police can only pursue complaints about noise if the noise endangers the security or order. A danger to the public security exists when noise endangers health. Whether this is the case can only be determined in each instance. Though noise without harmful effect on health may not endanger security, it can, however, affect public order. That is first of all the case when the peace of night or rest on Sundays and holidays is unnecessarily disturbed; also when it lowers man's work capacity."

Although many European cities are noisy, many of them have regulations covering noise sources often not covered by American municipal codes. For example, bicycles with auxiliary motors, which are very popular in Denmark, are also very much of a nuisance. According to the traffic code of the Danish Ministry of Justice, which supervises most driving and traffic regulations, the motors of such bicycles "shall be equipped with an effective device for reducing the sound and it shall be kept in a secure state." In 1959, special instructions were issued for measuring a specific noise limit (79 decibels at 7 meters), and at the same time a mobile noise control center was established under the jurisdiction of the state police.

Germany and Switzerland protect noise receivers on Sundays and holidays. Special Sunday and holiday laws ban all work performed in public that could disturb the peace. During the main hours of religious services, all possibly disturbing work must cease. In Germany, to reduce traffic noise on Sundays and holidays, there is a statute forbidding trucks (over a certain weight) to drive between the hours of midnight and 10:00 P.M.

Is it possible to produce a quiet jet airplane? Though the ultimate answer is cloaked in ambiguity and controversy, the general impression seems to be that aircraft could be designed to generate tolerable noise levels—at a cost. The ideal would be to start from scratch and develop a form of propulsion in which design for quiet was given as much weight as design for speed, power, and operating efficiency. Some believe this could be done if we made the same financial commitment to developing quiet subsonic aircraft as we are making to develop the SST.

Not only have we failed to make such a commitment, we find every step towards quiet design impeded by dollar signs. A March 1966 report of the Office of Science and Technology concluded that "In general, it is technically possible to suppress the noise of an exhaust jet, however, it is very costly in terms of percent of aircraft gross weight and installed hardware."

The Federal government has embarked on a jet noise allevia-tion program involving modifications in air frame and engine design, airport planning, modified flight procedures, and public relations programs. It is not expected that the "quieter engine" will solve the noise problem without moving noise away from the people by means of air traffic procedures, and keeping people away from the noise by zoning to keep residential development at a distance where complaints will be minimal. Sometime in 1972 the FAA in cooperation with NASA hopes to have a quiet engine, some 20 Perceived Noise Decibels quieter than present jet engines. This research engine will provide 50 hours of flight testing. The program is budgeted at $50 million.

In essence, our research goal is for a jet engine quiet enough to reduce the number of vigorous complaints.

To decrease the number of people who will be exposed to jet noise, airports may employ "preferred" runways, runways pointed away from land with dense residential development. Unfortunately, however, uncertain weather conditions and airport congestion tend to interfere with the preferred runway concept. Even if fewer homes, through new airport planning, are noise-impacted, those homeowners who are affected will still suffer.

There have been suggestions for changes in procedure such as slowing planes down, increasing their glide angle, and so forth. Pilots resist these practices on the grounds that they diminish certain safety margins. Indeed, it is stated in the jet-noise report cited above that modifying approach/takeoff procedures can pose safety problems.

With proper planning, new airports and heliports would not be sited where they can destroy livability. America's planning officials have access to guidelines provided by the FAA to keep from making glaring errors in deciding how far from the airport residential construction and development ought to take place. (An impartial analysis of these guidelines is needed to make sure they provide a desirable environment, and not one acceptable in the terms of the aviation industry.)

Name a vehicle noise source, and it can be tamed. Road reflection from the underside of the motor? Enclose the motor, as did the London Transport Company. Noisy road surface? Use smooth asphalt. Aerodynamic noise? Design the body elements to reduce turbulence.

The automotive industry has at its disposal an incredible array of acoustic expertise. GM alone has about 100 men assigned to its acoustic research section, and headed until his recent retirement by David Apps, an international authority on automotive noise control. The Ford Motor Company has a noise-vibration-harshness research team whose job it is to cope with some 15,000 sound-producing components of a car. The quest is to eliminate some of these sounds, insulate others, and convert the stubborn ones into pleasing sounds for the passenger.

Even the cabs of trucks are being sound-insulated, because drivers and their assistants have been opting for quietness for radio listening and off-duty sleep.

But, let us remember that these noise-control efforts are primarily directed toward driver and passenger comfort, not toward the noise recipients outside the vehicle.

The American Trucking Association claims that methods and techniques for muffling truck exhaust are well known to truck manufacturers and that consequently there is no excuse for offending trucks to be coming off assembly lines.

Manufacturers can do more for quieter trucks than simply installing better mufflers. They can modify the design of air cleaners, fans, fuel injection and air intake systems. Mechanical noises from transmission and chassis could also be designed out.

The chassis GM used for New York City's garbage trucks was designed with more than a superior exhaust system. The engine itself was quieted by a number of innovations, ranging from a dry-element air cleaner to a five-blade, staggered configuration fan. The fan itself is enclosed in a shroud to reduce noise radiation from the engine housing. To purchasers of these quieter trucks GM recommended the use of tire treads designed to make less noise.

According to the motor vehicle manufacturers, the rubber tire manufacturers are slow to design less noise producing tires. To encourage both quieter tire design and quieter vehicle design, local governments could require lower speed limits for nighttime driving.

Motorcycle noise, in common with that of other motor vehicles, would be severely reduced if the public would ask for proper design, and enforce its demands in the act of purchasing. CQC proved this in December 1967. At a public demonstration the audience recoiled as a motorcycle was started up. The sound level meter read a hefty 110 decibels at 15 feet. The bike was stopped. When it was started up again, the observers heard only an astonishing muted purr: 70 decibels at 15 feet. A 40-decibel reduction. Why the difference?

In the "before" demonstration, the muffler had been removed. To control motorcycle noise a quality muffler is an essential. But so is quiet design. This motorcycle was unique in advertising that it was designed for quiet—and its claim stood up in demonstration.

Though difficult to accomplish in large cities, major arteries can be sited away from residential and other noise-sensitive areas, neighborhood traffic flow reduced by using bypass roads for through traffic, and the noise of stop-and-go driving eliminated by using cloverleafs and Y-interchanges. When all else fails, barriers can be placed between the roadway and the human target.

The Russians, to avoid traffic-noise problems in new towns, set up small models of building blocks representing residential, commercial, and industrial areas. Tests are conducted to see how simulated traffic noise is to be kept from the residential area by using the non-residential buildings as barriers.

Other methods for reducing the amount of noise radiating from the road include depressed road construction, the use of flanking barriers, and covering the surface with plastic materials that absorb tire noise.

Chicago has built "groove ways" or depressed roads for its highway from the Loop to O'Hare Airport. When it is not feasible to depress a roadway, planners can try high shoulders, with landscaping. The Russians are experimenting with barriers on expressways in new city districts. These barriers are earth banks three meters high along each side of the road, terraced down to the buildings and topped with reinforced concrete screens. The topping will be planted with trees.

Architect Morris Ketchum points across the Atlantic to Cumbernauld, a new town in Scotland, where the city and traffic live together in harmony. Its center expressway is depressed and framed by earthen banks. Shopping, offices, and theaters all border this main street. Most of the residential buildings are set at right angles to motorways so that sound cannot reverberate among them. "It is a quiet city."

Recognizing the difficulty of reducing the daily din of life, towns in Austria, Germany, France, and Switzerland have instituted "quiet zones" in which vehicular traffic is *verboten* during certain hours of the day and night. An example is France's Vittell Thermal Spa. In response to many complaints about traffic noise, and to protect the peace of summer vacationists, a Quiet Zone was created within the thermal bath quarters. Traffic of all motor vehicles—including motorcycles—is prohibited between 10:00 P.M. and 7:00 A.M. After 10:00 P.M. access to the main part of town, which houses the major hotels, is achieved via roads that lead to large parking zones, which are situated close to the hotels. Newcomers entering the town are informed of the regulations. Enforcement has been no problem.

The ramifications of this "quiet zone" should give the auto industry pause. Here is a case in which society says it will not bother with methods of reducing noise, but will eliminate it by banning the source.

Attempts to curb auto horn blowing began soon after the first horn was blown. The curse of the horn is worldwide, and so are the legislative attempts to lift it.

There are several approaches available today for curbing this irritant. Limits on the intensity and tonal quality can stimulate design of an auto horn that emits pleasing tones, with upper limits set for loudness.

The need for horn blowing can be reduced by substituting an overtaking or passing light system. A special position on the direction-signal switch arm activates head lamps as an effective signal in the daytime. At night, in place of sound signals, the use of such anti-dazzling lights at short intervals is relied on. Austria, for example, minimizes the need to use a horn by requiring that automobiles be equipped with an optical device that flashes intermittently, but without any dazzle. This type of special passing light system is illegal in the United States.

Paris is the pioneer in horn control. Sometime before 1930 the Prefect of Police there made use of horns unlawful after midnight:

> Drivers are compelled to slacken the pace of their vehicle everywhere needed, in particular at crossroads, so as to make it useless to use a horn.
>
> Art. 2—Infractions of the provisions of this ordinance will be recorded in orders to pay a fine which will be forwarded to the competent courts.

Drivers learned that they could operate as safely without acoustic warnings as with them, and grew to rely on the auto horn less during the day, also. It was natural that the ban would then be extended (1954) to daytime driving as well.

New York followed Paris in enacting an anti-horn blowing ordinance—one more respected in the breach than in the observance, and one the police seem to enforce in ten-year cycles.

December 18, 1967, was a red-letter day in the American noise abatement movement. The locale was the side of the reflecting pool at that citadel of culture, Lincoln Center for the Performing Arts. The invited guests were important enough—two Congressmen (Theodore Kupferman and William F. Ryan), representatives from the Mayor's office and his task force on noise control, representatives of American manufacturers of pneumatic construction equipment, and members of the press. The star of the occasion was a yellow two-wheeled contraption imported from England, something never before publicly demonstrated in the United States, and not being manufactured here: a silenced portable air compressor. Thanks to the English business contacts of Anthony Essex Potter, CQC Board Member, and a British construction equipment manufacturer, Holman Bros., CQC was able to inform the American public that unmuffled construction noise was not necessary.

Several months later, Ingersoll-Rand announced a quieter American two-wheeled compressor, and then topped this with the marketing of a silenced giant four-wheeled compressor (900 cfm) that generated 85 decibels at 1 meter, instead of 105 decibels. Thus was started a gradual move to introduce a degree of quiet design into pneumatic construction equipment. It is taking more than five years of my life, but the days of raw, uncontrolled construction noise are numbered. In April 1970, I was informed by Joy Manufacturing Company that it was introducing a complete line of quieter compressors, ranging from 175 cfm to 1,200 cfm. The design goal was 85 decibels at 1 meter for a premium of 25 per cent, and 90 decibels at 1 meter for an increase in cost of 10 per cent. Electric air compressors, heretofore kept under wraps by their manufacturers, are now being used for tunnel projects, and for public works sites where militant residents insist on quieter operations. The first electric compressor I experienced was in 1966 in Zurich. Serving a major street renovation project, it was, compared to the monsters on Sixth Avenue, almost a joy to hear. And no dense diesel fumes on-site.

At that same Lincoln Center demonstration, co-star billing was given to two jackhammers with built-in mufflers, one imported from Holman Bros. and the other discovered in the catalogue of Chicago Pneumatic Tool Co. Both were some hefty 10 decibels less than their noisy unmuffled competitors.

There is nothing impractical about jackhammers with built-in mufflers. The principles governing Holman's design improvement are: 1) the performance of the machine cannot be noticeably reduced, 2) its bulk or weight cannot be increased to the point where it becomes difficult to handle, and 3) the additional cost is to be moderate.

Today other American companies are making quieter jackhammers, and one puts out an accessory muffler that fits around the shaft of any regular jackhammer. Electric hammers are available and eliminate the punch of the pneumatic exhaust. The French are marketing, in the United States, hydraulic paving-breakers with a patented treatment of the internal piston that reduces much of the noise from that source. They combine the breaker with a small silenced compressor as a special package for utility company night work. Hughes Tool Company markets a rotary "cookie cutter" that quietly cuts circular holes in pavement. The primitive mechanical pile driver, with its day-long pounding and pounding, can be silenced by substituting the hydraulic and sonic equipment now on the market.

Of course, *silencing* is a relative term. For example, what has been accomplished is not to make construction noise a desirable neighbor, but at least to soften some of the naked sounds of construction machinery.

The question always raised is: what noise level? The German Health Ministry realizes existing knowledge does not permit drawing a hard and fast line to divide health-injuring noise from noise that is merely "annoying." Lacking a specific exposure limit (combination of time and noise level), Germany nevertheless seeks to promulgate laws requiring the reduction of intense noise—*at its sources.* In 1965 the West German government put noise curbs on construction projects.

The operator of construction machinery must see to it that all noises which, according to the latest technical developments, it is possible to avoid or minimize *are* avoided or minimized, and also see to it that the emanation of unavoidable noises from the construction site be kept to the absolute minimum possible. The operation of a machine that does not comply with these stipulations can be prohibited until the noise is reduced. This is much more effective than a fine.

Switzerland was regulating construction noise before 1965. In 1964, Zurich's noise control office investigated 303 construction sites. Several projects were shut down until the contractors found methods to reduce noise. Austria makes possible an immediate reduction in construction-equipment noise by applying an existing law, the gist of which is that noise made in an "improper" manner is punishable. If noise emanates from a tool that is not technically up to date, it could be interpreted to be an "improperly" made noise. Compressed air equipment lacking muffling would fall into this category.

In America, regulatory agencies, such as the Transit Authority, have the power to curb construction noise without any new legislation. All they have to do is enforce the silencing clause that is standard in many contracts awarded by public agencies. Could any wording be more explicit, or more completely ignored, than the silencing clause in the subway extension contract between the Transit Authority and the contractors? "The contractor must perform all work in such a manner as to create a minimum of noise. He may be required to shield or otherwise cover or insulate his operations so as to restrict the transmission of noise . . . (he) shall be solely responsible for the performance of the work in a manner which will not create or constitute objectionable noise or other nuisance to the public. . . ."

It is difficult for the urban apartment dweller to believe that the United States National Bureau of Standards was testing home sound insulation as long ago as 1922! It has been publishing the results of such testing since 1939. Its latest guide to noise control in dwellings was published in 1967.

Builders and architects know the laboratory-tested values of more than a hundred varieties of door, floor, and wall constructions. They can get design information from the FHA, and from companies that specialize in noise-rated construction products, such as Owens-Corning and U.S. Gypsum. With this information they can select the proper sound-insulating wall, a floor construction that stops the noise of your neighbors' footsteps, and the proper materials for halls, doors, windows, as well as techniques for plugging acoustic leaks in piping and wiring openings in walls and floors and installing plumbing and appliances to operate quietly.

The builder and designer can specify the sound-insulating quality of the wall partition desired, as well as floor/ceiling construction. Methods of evaluating the acoustic quality of a finished room have been used in the Netherlands since 1948.

Mechanical equipment—such as central air conditioning motors and dishwashers—can be mounted on isolation mounts on special flooring to prevent sound transmission. Pipes can be isolated from the building structure to prevent converting the structure into a sounding box. Plumbing noises can be eliminated by proper choice of fixtures and careful installation.

One undesirable feature of air conditioning (and mechanical ventilating) is the noise made by rushing air. This noise can be controlled by reducing the velocity of the air stream, lining the air ducts with sound-absorbent materials, or equipping the outlets with mufflers. Fan noise can be reduced by increasing the number of fan blades and staggering the design of the blades to prevent the formation of irritating tones.

The noise of mechanical ventilating and central air conditioning, with its noisy air flow and cooling tower noise, is controllable. ASHRAE, the professional society of the industry, has published detailed technical reports on how to sound-control all types of air conditioning installations. It has evolved a system of noise standards and criteria for single-family homes, apartment houses, churches, offices and schools.

As a matter of fact, silencing techniques are so sophisticated, one company puts out a Short Form for busy designers to use in "calculating the amount and type of noise control desired." Noisy systems can also be quieted after installation. It is cheaper, however, to introduce noise control at the design stage.

A small detail such as not installing medicine cabinets in the walls and back to back will help eliminate noise transmission between bathrooms.

American Standard advertises a deluxe model kitchen garbage disposal unit that "is a conversation piece . . . because every word praising it will be easily heard." If this advertising copy is accurate, the disposal is quiet because the outer shell is constructed of heavy, extra thick fiber glass insulation with a shock-absorbent rubber mounting that cushions noise and minimizes vibration.

Builders, especially in a competitive market, will not incorporate noise control provisions without an incentive. That incentive can be made a part of local building codes by requiring that in addition to standards for fireproofing and safety, homes be built to noise insulation standards. Europeans have long recognized the need for government to provide this incentive. Germany led the way in 1938, and since then, building codes including noise specifications have been adopted in Austria, Belgium, Denmark, England, Finland, France, the Netherlands, Norway, Scotland, Sweden, and Switzerland; not to mention Bulgaria, Czechoslovakia, and the Soviet Union.

Apparently, not all of these countries require that private building meet their national standards. However, private builders, as in Switzerland, are encouraged to adhere to them, by the realization that a new tenant who finds himself deprived of the peaceful use of his apartment can go to court and obtain a rent reduction.

Zoning is a traditional form of noise control. Its use, legend has it, goes back to the days of the ancient Sybarites, who some 2,500 years ago were intelligent enough to exclude blacksmithing, cabinetmaking, and other noisy industries from the residential city.

Zoning ordinances are used today primarily to protect residential areas from noises made *within* factories and commercial installations. Decibel limits are set on the amount of noise that can be radiated from within the factory to its boundary.

In Czechoslovakia, factories that produce noise exceeding 100 decibels must have a protective belt of 500 meters, and the external noise level at the point nearest any residential area must not exceed 50 decibels by day or 40 decibels at night. In the Soviet Union, plants with equipment causing a noise level over 90 decibels must be located on the leeward side of the nearest residential area and separated from it by an acoustic buffer zone, landscaped and planted with trees. Beyond this zone the noise must not exceed a specified level.

In Germany, certain industries have to receive a permit before being able to build or operate a plant, and this permit will only be granted if all technical advances are harnessed in the interest of noise abatement. Should an installation not abide with this regulation, the permit may be withdrawn.

The zoning concept can be expanded to offer protection from many undesirable noises. Coral Gables, Florida, applies zoning to noises made within the home, especially to residential air conditioning systems, to protect neighbors from each other and give them freedom from unnecessary noise. Unnecessary is interpreted to mean capable of being muffled, or designed to make less noise. By placing air conditioner noise control in a zoning ordinance instead of the typical anti-noise ordinance, Coral Gables avoided the impasse of having to establish a case for health damage.

(In reviewing some of the few statutory limitations on air conditioning, I asked a consulting engineer if society wasn't being too harsh on the industry, since there were no universal standards. He replied, "They don't need special standards to make an air conditioner that permits room conversation without straining my voice.")

Dallas, Texas, offers an example of how a public health department can utilize a zoning ordinance. In that city, the health department regulations use the noise standards incorporated in the Dallas Zoning Ordinance. The Village of Port Washington, on Long Island, used its zoning code to prohibit a company from using part of its industrial-zoned property for a private helicopter site. Where there is a commitment, there is a way.

As a last resort, a specific noise source can be banned.

One of the first sources to go in recent history was the *poubelle*, the French garbage can. In Paris, household *poubelles* must be of a design that permits noiseless handling of the lid and the can body. The ordinance introduced in 1959 gave householders until January 1, 1963—three years—to replace existing cans; after that date, those that did not meet the "noiseless" specifications were not emptied.

In the United States at least one local government arranged the banning of automatically operated bells, chimes, and gongs used on ice cream trucks. When enforcement of a curfew on sound signals after 9:00 P.M. proved impossible, New York City's former Markets Commissioner Gerard Weisberg took action. He acknowledged the benefits of mobile ice cream vending: convenience and the summer employment offered young people on vacation. He only objected to the nuisance value of the automated signals. In 1968 he issued a new regulation, making their use illegal. He figured that a vendor with hand bells would be too busy dispensing ice cream to ring the bell often enough to create a nuisance in the neighborhood.

Administrative regulations and licensing are not the only means available to government for achieving quiet. Government agencies can specify quiet design when purchasing traditionally noisy machines and equipment. This is what New York City did to some degree when it was replacing its fleet of garbage trucks. If a silent submarine can be ordered to "tuned" frequency specifications, so can garbage trucks, air compressors, and jackhammers. Municipal governments will need to learn how to cooperate with vendors to achieve design goals.

The public will have to insist that a rigid bidding system in government does not stifle noise abatement. The manufacturer of the quieter products should be rewarded with a purchase order.

Though this book emphasizes the noises of machines, there is also the important category of people-made noises, noises that could be eliminated by the exercise of personal discretion.

Assuming that the motorcycle as manufactured was designed for quiet operation, the motorcyclist could control the amount of noise his vehicle emits by accelerating slowly, refraining from revving his motor while idling, not removing or de-activating his muffler. Motorcycle trade associations, sensitive to anti-motorcycle sentiment and fearful of restrictive legislation, caution their customers to be good neighbors. In a booklet given to purchasers, they urge the cyclist not to remove the internal baffles of his muffler, add cut-outs, replace quality mufflers with cheap ones, or, worse yet, with "Hollywood type" megaphone mufflers. As an incentive not to tamper with the muffler, the Motorcycle, Scooter and Allied Trades Association cautions cyclists that the excessive noise generated by "adjusted" mufflers may actually reduce the performance of the engine, increase engine temperature, burn out valves, and create other conditions that will impair or destroy the efficiency of the power plant.

All manufacturers of radios and other volume-controlled noise emitters should provide some means of urging volume reduction, especially at night. The use of portable radios in public places can be controlled by local ordinance. In France the prefects of the individual departments were given this instruction: ". . . transistorized apparatus may only be used in public with their loud speakers turned off (use earphones only)." In England and Wales no one may use a radio in public so as to cause annoyance, and radios are specifically prohibited in London's Hyde Park. Local buses in Washington, D.C. ban radios.

People can eliminate many noise problems by proper behavior. Housewives using noisy appliances can stop during meal hours, and certainly avoid mechanical cleaning during hours of sleep. Pianists can install damping devices on their instruments so that their practicing does not convert adjacent apartments into concert halls. An attempt can be made to restrict the noisy play of children to non-sensitive locations. Dogs can be trained not to bark, and parents can implant in their children a good example of acoustic manners by driving without excessive use of the auto horn.

People are all too frequently unaware of how their noisemaking activities impinge on their neighbors. Requests for quiet are interpreted as personal attacks, and raise hackles. There is growing interest in the Swedish concept of a third-party intermediary, the ombudsman, an official who can function as the citizen's advisor, and champion his grievances against the injustices of government, or help him if he finds he must take his neighbors to court.

At the same time that man's seeming obsession with speed and convenience have generated the noisiest epoch in his history, his intelligence has produced the means of enjoying the fruits of technology without suffering from its acoustic waste products. What is needed is a widespread concern for protecting the human being and his environment from excessive noise. Were there such concern the making of noisy products would soon become illegal. Will anybody care?

CHAPTER NINE

Promises, Promises

Without commitment, noise abatement is a possibility, not a probability. At the time this book was being written, few scientists, few manufacturers, and few lawmakers believed that noise abatement warranted a place on mankind's shopping list. Whether or not the straws in the wind discussed in this chapter are to be precursors of action will depend upon how effectively the informed can convince the insensitive and the indifferent that there is a noise problem.

Will noise abatement ride in on the coattails of the new movement for environmental quality? This will depend upon the long-run success of that movement, and how seriously its leaders take noise as a factor in the environment.

There is a chance that noise abatement will benefit from the new attempt to humanize science and technology, to inculcate new attitudes toward human beings which would require that they be spared the stress and cruelty of noxious noise exposure.

215

Bruited around in some scientific circles is the novel concept that the ultimate purpose of life might be man himself. At the 75th Anniversary celebration of that citadel of science, the California Institute of Technology, scientists told fellow scientists to base their standards on moral, cultural, and spiritual values. "Somehow people must be made to expand their sense of loyalty and responsibility to include a larger share of the human race," said one speaker. The scientists were urged to start feeling for the human beings who would be living in the environments they are changing.

The physicist and the engineer, at their technical and professional society meetings, in the pages of their technical and professional society meetings, in the pages of their professional and trade magazines, are being made to realize they have ignored the human being as a receiver of noise. "If engineers were asked to describe a human being they probably would depict a creature without ears . . . Engineers should refuse to specify materials and equipment for residences, office buildings, hospitals and schools that will not allow human beings to function in peace and quiet," said an article in the March 1969 issue of *Consulting Engineer.* It would have impressed me more were I not its author. Nevertheless, it is significant that the concerned citizen was invited by this magazine to express his views.

Engineer published Congressman Kupferman's challenge to the excuse that noise is a necessary price of industrial and economic progress. That idea, he said, "is as antiquated as is the belief contaminated water and a polluted atmosphere must also accompany civilization's advances."

An editorial in *Product Engineering* (July 29, 1968) reminded the conscientious engineer that "In the products he designs in his professional career, he can fight as hard for quiet in lawn mowers and all the rest as he fights for efficiency, durability, and safety."

One even finds thinkers in the think tanks telling their associates that their future role should be serving the total community without concern for the manufacturer or for profit.

This belated interest in human needs is reaching the colleges and universities. There seems to be a growing awareness that engineers need an education and not merely engineering training. As president of Rose Polytechnic Institute, Dr. John A. Logan called for a new kind of engineering education that would develop specialists concerned about the use of science and technology for the well-being of man. He believes that engineers must be taught how to use the humanities to make the world a more pleasant place in which to live. To this far-seeing educator, comfort and aesthetics are just as important factors in environmental health as disease control

As the number of farmers decreases, the agricultural colleges are seeking legitimate new directions. They are concerned with developing nutrition and home economics programs that can be applied to the urban low-income groups. They are concerned with air pollution. There is no reason why extension divisions of agricultural colleges could not move on noise control. Rutgers University's College of Agricultural and Environmental Sciences, in sponsoring noise pollution symposia, has already begun to move in this direction.

Signs of a people-and-environment interest are beginning to appear in the practice of medicine and in other professions. In 1969, McGraw-Hill's *Medical World News* began a series on man's threatened environment with a story on noise reporting that physicians "are increasingly alarmed" at the continuous exposure of human beings to today's everyday noises.

The American Public Health Association is slowly responding to pressure to recognize that noise is a health issue. It is encouraging that not only did the American Public Health Association invite me to present a paper critical of its neglect, but it subsequently published "Noise and Urban Man" in its *Journal.* In a recent revision of its principles for housing design, proper noise insulation within dwellings was described as essential to health. It was also recommended that homes containing children and the aged should be protected from the noises of busy highways.

Some members of the legal profession are recognizing the need to protect man in the reasonable enjoyment of his property, and that to meet this need the excesses of technology must be curbed. On August 3, 1968, the *Saturday Review* devoted a section to the question: Can the law relate to the physical and life sciences in a manner that will protect not only the human body but human dignity? Its contributors answered in the affirmative, and saw the lawyer of the future, given the proper social orientation, as one who could help oversee the technical experts who now dominate the decisionmaking process.

It is encouraging to hear the outspoken contention of European practicing and teaching lawyers that the role of law is to protect man from the machine, and not the reverse. Zurich seems to be a center for this humanist thinking, and men like Dr. Schenker-Sprüngli, Professor M. Keller, and Professor K. Oftinger take the position that the law must set limits to technology: that the purpose of law is to enforce moral values. "The right to live undisturbed is a fundamental right of the individual rooted in the law," says Schenker-Sprüngli. These men raise the question of the legality of invading the privacy of the home with disturbing sonic booms.

American conservationists are developing a legal attack on environmental pollution. The Scenic Hudson Preservation Conference fought to keep Con Edison from constructing a facility on Storm King Mountain that would have caused thermal pollution of the Hudson River. The Environmental Defense Fund fights in the courts to stop the indiscriminate use of DDT. The Conservation Foundation is developing a modus operandi for a legal defense of the environment. CQC is encouraging law students and young practicing lawyers to explore legal attacks on noisemaking. In time society will see there is not too much difference between poisoning fish and animal life with DDT and poisoning man with dB(A).

One of the four points of the "conservation bill of rights" includes reduction of excessive noise. New York State voters were given the opportunity to vote on this amendment to their constitution on November 3, 1969, and they approved it. A similar amendment has been proposed for the Federal Constitution. Once enacted, such amendments serve as a prod to make legislators enact implementing statutes.

If the conservationists win, cities, too, may become quieter. Any machine that must be muffled in the natural environment will eventually keep its muffler on in the urban environment.

There is evidence American architects are beginning to recognize the public has ears. Architect Samuel Paul dedicated his book *Apartments, Their Design and Development* to "People." Published in 1967, this book contained a chapter on sound control written by his son David J. Paul, who foresees the day when sound control treatment will be standard practice in all apartment construction.

The New York Chapter of the American Institute of Architects has initiated an annual environmental awards program to encourage design to make the city more livable. In January 1969 it awarded CQC a citation "For their acute awareness in advocating noise abatement."

One of Expo 67's major exhibits was Habitat, a new concept in dwellings that featured acoustic as well as visual privacy.

Foreign architects seem to be more active in promoting protection from noise than American architects. Canada's Royal Architectural Institute has called upon architects to design enclosed spaces not only to protect workers from hearing loss, but to save the general population from noise-induced tension and fatigue. Nothing in the United States has matched the memorandum submitted in 1960 to the Wilson Committee by the Royal

Institute of British Architects. This group pointed out that they cannot control the environment in which their designed buildings are to be located, and that government has a patent responsibility for environmental control.

The memorandum also took to task the aviation ministry's favorable report on heliports in the London area. Unlike their American counterparts who are still unaware of what center-city aviation means, these architects made it clear that helicopters in Central London would mean "that the whole of Central London . . . will be subjected to noise levels equivalent to those on the pavements of Oxford Street; in the neighborhood of the helicopter station they will, of course, be very much higher . . . . We are greatly perturbed at the loss of a sense of social values it betokens." The Institute recommended rapid surface or underground transportation to the airports, and protection of residential areas from heavy traffic.

It was also recommended that the building construction industries set up a development program for quieter methods of operation. The key to the problem of industrial noise, the Institute pointed out, is in the hands of machinery designers.

Other recommendations included compulsory noise rating for machinery, the conversion into law of recommended sound insulation standards in buildings, and the development of a method whereby the people who create noise, not their victims, should be made responsible for spending money to control it.

This type of memorandum not only clarifies the issues for government, but gives the public a valuable base for its noise abatement efforts.

There is already the beginning of a crack in the wall separating the "expert" and the public, the beginning of a dialogue wherein both can exchange their views. In 1967 it was unusual for a promoter of noise abatement, thought of as "the other side," to find himself offered a platform at the 74th semi-annual meeting of the Acoustical Society of America. Yet a surprising number of the acousticians in the audience responded favorably to my thesis that the noise expert was neglecting his everyday human environment. One of them, speaking of his participation in the meeting, said: "It helps me to be a better acoustician in the civic sense."

The Acoustical Society subsequently invited Dr. Rosen, CQC's Board Chairman, to address its 77th semi-annual meeting. Papers on urban noise are proliferating.

One thing I learned in speaking to regional groups of noise experts: the rank and file has more of a people-orientation than the policymakers. There is a deep-seated desire to hear the public's point of view, and an eagerness to learn more about how to participate in the campaign for noise abatement.

Acousticians are starting to listen to criticism of their esoteric, incomprehensible decibel world. As president of the Acoustical Society, Ira Hirsch conceded: "Our scientific jargon is not easily communicated to those who must quiet our noise sources, who must build the buildings in which people live or work, who must write the codes or municipal laws to protect the citizen, or who must enforce such codes . . . . We must be willing to share our knowledge while translating it into ordinary English and algebra . . . ."

Note the novel objective written into the preliminary report of one standards writing group: "The ultimate goal is to achieve a maximum amount of human privacy from intrusion by noise and vibration acoustically induced." The people-oriented chairman of this group had appointed a sociologist and an informed member of the lay public to work with the representatives of industry and the acousticians.

In a letter to parsons that appeared in *Gegen den Lärm*, the magazine of the Swiss Noise Abatement League, the president and director of the League raised religious reasons for fighting noise:

For the Christian, silence is a prerequisite of the spiritual disposition, for in silence he is able to perceive the voice of God. Already in the Old Testament was this connection evident. Often in the New Testament one reads of how Jesus went out into the wilderness. . . . If He, the Son of God, felt a need for silence, He, who . . . never fell under the influence of His surroundings, how much more do we need that stillness in order to come before God in silence! Uncounted numbers of men can no longer find this inner quiet amid the daily ever-present noise, and they thereby lack the natural basis for the deeper delving or believing to take place . . . .

The Swiss are not the only ones seeking commitment from clergymen. In the United States, the first president of Citizens for a Quieter City was Jerome Nathanson, a Leader of the Society for Ethical Culture; Rabbi Edward E. Klein and Rev. Frederick M. Morris, D.D., are charter members of its Advisory Board. In what may have been the first such address in the United States, Mr. Nathanson presented an Ethical Culture Sunday Platform on the subject "Can We Have a Quieter New York?" Among his points: "Whatever in the environment undercuts or adversely affects people in their relationship is plainly unethical . . . . Unquestionably the human environment we have been building in this city, as well as in cities throughout the country and the world, [has] been destructive of human well-being . . . . A quieter city is part of the civilization we deserve and must achieve."

Rev. Morris, Rector of St. Thomas Church in New York, asks his parishioners to use their influence to support a reasonable control of unnecessary noise. And Rabbi Klein was active in preventing the West Side STOLport from being built in the middle of a congested residential and cultural complex.

Even the business community is beginning to realize that restrictive legislation is the result, not of anti-business bias, but of the public's dissatisfaction with abuses. Enlightened businessmen are warning their colleagues that business has a stake in preserving the city. "If we fail to improve those surroundings," cautioned Ralph Lazarus, president of Federated Department Stores, "the resulting anger and frustration will inevitably break about our heads." Life insurance companies, owners of some ghetto buildings, have taken out full-page ads in newspapers across the country to warn that traffic noise as well as slums is making second-class citizens of poor and rich alike.

The Portland, Oregon, Chamber of Commerce started with an environmental committee and now has added a noise subcommittee. That same city's City Club has a committee on noise. And New York's Board of Trade is sponsoring an all-inclusive Business Council for Environmental Protection.

Another illustration of business community involvement was the substantial contribution to CQC made by Scali, McCabe and Sloves, a young New York advertising agency. Not only did this agency prepare public service newspaper and magazine ads and radio messages, it helped out with office space and other contributions.

Even the noisemaker has begun to commit himself to noise abatement. The chairman of that New York Council is William I. Wearly, top executive of Ingersoll-Rand, manufacturers of construction equipment. James W. Wilcock, president of Joy Manufacturing Company, is on the Honorary Board of CQC. Both men are becoming leaders in the design of quieter construction equipment.

From drills for concrete to drills for teeth, manufacturers are beginning to sense a demand for quiet products. Quiet is becoming a competitive feature. Enlightened self-interest is at work.

One reason Bethlehem Steel agreed to develop a quieter metal garbage can for CQC was the threat of competition from new plastic and paper containers. Encouraged by the national and international interest in that quieter can, Bethlehem has embarked upon a new program to provide a noise control service to other users of its metal stock, manufacturers of dishwashers for one. Owens-Corning has a giant acoustic facility to help develop quieter appliances and architectural products for its clients.

Business is motivated to design for quiet by the thought of benefits from noise control, or, conversely, the threat of some form of loss. Standard Oil (New Jersey) sought goodwill when it built a new refinery. It took out institutional ads to let the public know its new installation was going to be a quiet neighbor.

At the public demonstration of his firm's quieter giant air compressor, Ingersoll-Rand's Wearly observed that the development of this improved equipment "reflects I-R's concern not only to be an innovator among manufacturers of machinery, equipment and tools, but to be a good neighbor as well. Undeniably construction is a noisy business. However, it is our aim— through research—to reduce noise to a level that will not trouble citizens of the communities in which we live and work."

Whether or not business is convinced it must design for quiet, Madison Avenue sees sales in advertising quiet, and noisemakers are not as afraid as they once were to face the issue. In 1965 the one American company with a muffled jackhammer was publicity-shy. Chicago Pneumatic Tool, since the Lincoln Center demonstration, has redesigned its brochures and devoted its midtown Manhattan ground floor window to an attractive display of its quieter tool.

Gracious living is the reward promised for using Carvel Hall's non-motorized knives which carve silently. "Make friends with the People Downstairs," suggests one carpet ad. "It can be done. If they don't hear every step you take, every pin you drop, every word you say. Bedroom carpeting gives you privacy . . . . "

Aware of a growing resistance to sleepless nights, motels are advertising that they are located away from noisy highways. The Marriott Hotel chain invites businessmen to hold their meetings at their hotels, and after dinner enjoy a quiet sleeping room.

Mobil Gas advertises that its travel guide helps motorists find a quiet place to sleep. Mobil's inspector, the ads say, turns on all the noise sources in a motel—TV, heating, air conditioning—and then, turning them off, lies down in bed and keeps very quiet. He listens for noises from other rooms. One hopes he also listens for traffic noise and the noise of a Mobil or competitor's truck re-filling the oil tanks for the motel's heating system.

When New York's infamous utility Con Edison changed chiefs, the new chief, Charles Luce, admitted in full-page ads that when Con Ed dug it dug noisily. But, he added, Con Ed was now trying to do its digging more quietly, and was experimenting with silenced equipment. (It also set up a novel internal task force on noise abatement.)

Somehow or other the public must become aware of the sig-nificance of technological innovation before such innovations are locked-in to the environment. No sooner do we hear about an SST or V/STOL than they seem to become commercial reali-ties. It is encouraging that the mass media are slowly starting to provide quick communication so necessary to spark the needed debates and analyses. Not only are news stories describing what is happening, editorials are pressing for curbs and control. Net-work TV is starting to inform the public about the dangers of amplified music and New York's and Tokyo's noise problems. Local TV stations, at least in New York, Philadelphia, and a few other cities are producing noise pollution panel shows and docu-mentaries. *Newsweek, Time, Life, Fortune, Esquire, Playboy* and the *Readers Digest* now recognize noise pollution as part of the urban crisis.

The first "popular" national presentation of noise abatement took place on Johnny Carson's *Tonight* Show. Carson and his production staff deserve credit for demonstrating before millions of viewers the feasibility of noise control.

An unexpected dividend of that appearance may make noise abatement a household word. Actress Phyllis Newman, who was the next guest after the noise abatement segment, interjected her noise problems. and she and Carson discussed their personal noise hangups. Perhaps in the future celebrities on the widely-watched talk shows will discuss noise and similar environmental problems to which they are exposed, even as you and I.

Celebrities cannot do the job alone, and it is encouraging to report there is a trickle of volunteers in noise abatement work, people who will help with the day-to-day operations of an office. Citizens for a Quieter City, with its sometimes-less-than-shoe-string budget, would not have been able to function without the year's help of Mary Coughlin, a senior citizen who remembered her shorthand and typing; Anne Cavanaugh, who came for one week to "type some cards" and stayed for seven months until called away by marriage; Elizabeth Meffen, and Irene Ebeling, to mention a few.

Citizen movements, unless adequately financed, depend heavily on this type of participation. It is promising that noise victims are realizing they can help themselves, and others, by channeling some of their protest energy into helping an organized noise abatement operation.

It is promising too that some noise victims are reacting with directness. For example, when highway crews worked around the clock to complete a section of interstate highway near the University of Minnesota, indignant citizens telephoned the president of the construction company at four o'clock in the morning. He had not even known of their months of complaints about not being able to sleep at night. The victory they won was cessation of the project from midnight to 5:00 A.M.

More and more it appears that people are losing their tolerance for noise. If there were such a thing as a noise barometer, it would reach "Violence" on the scale of reactions. The chopping of air compressor hoses at construction sites, the shooting of bullets at low-flying jets, the actual murder of a horn-tooting motorist—these are but a few of the more startling individual incidents of violence brought on by an excessive noise problem and a frustrated citizenry.

Militant protest is becoming widespread. Noisy patrons

emerging from a Paris restaurant so irritated a tenant of the building, he took his rifle and wounded five men and women. Jet noise has provoked bomb threats and assaults with a variety of projectiles. A mother of three, living near Kennedy Airport, allegedly telephoned a threat to bomb the control tower. "I couldn't stand it anymore, the low-flying jets," she told a reporter. "They frightened my children, rattled the house, made me a nervous wreck." Would milk of magnesia have relieved her tension?

A $20,000-a-year business executive, naively believing he was buying an escape from city noise, purchased a farm home near Dayton. To his extreme annoyance, he found himself under the flight path of low-flying Air Force jets. Unable to secure any accommodation, he took five shots at the jets. He was placed on probation, and forced to move.

The most publicized incident is the one involving artist Helmut Winter, the *"Kartofel Werfer"* of suburban Munich. Winter suddenly found his home under the flight path of low-flying Luftwaffe and U.S. Air Force jets. When his complaints, like the Dayton man's, were to no avail, he built a modified version of the Roman ballista, a sort of powerful slingshot, and used this device as an anti-aircraft gun—loading it, however, with potato dumplings instead of shells. The frightening plop of dumpling on fuselage did what all else had failed to do: it got the flight path changed. Winter became an international hero. He won the acclaim of noise victims around the world because he had acted out —in his own fashion—what they probably had fantasized for years.

Auto horns appear to be exceptional provokers of violence. On a December day in 1966, one motorist picked an unfortunate place to honk his horn, outside a trailer camp where an obviously mentally-disturbed tenant kept a gun. The horn-happy driver was silenced, forever, with a bullet, and the sniper, after shooting it out with the police, committed suicide. He left a note explaining, "Every day from 4:00 to 6:00 P.M. the constant honking of horns made life unbearable for everyone, including me." One wire service story noted that the radio in the killer's trailer was blaring at the time of the incident. An attempt to mask the passing horns?

Shortly after I opened the office of CQC a friendly police official tipped me off that Con Edison* had received an unsigned typed letter threatening to "get" the jackhammer operator on Sixth Avenue who started up at such an early hour every morning on a street-opening project. No, it was not my typewriter.

Some years ago two men got together in hopes of marketing a battery-operated car for $600. The delivery date was never met because of problems of low speeds, limited driving range, high cost, and the great weight of the batteries. The two men were Thomas Edison and Henry Ford. Today, more than half a century later, quiet substitutes for the internal combustion engine are still little more than promises, except that the types of substitutes have increased and the development and application show some signs of progress. Rushing to meet that 1915 delivery date, Ford now claims a breakthrough with the development of a battery that promises to meet the need for an efficient, low-cost, compact urban/suburban electric vehicle requiring only an overnight charge. Time will tell.

Engineers are going even further back in history to re-examine the Stanley Steamer. General Motors is testing a thermal engine for the Army, one reported to be extremely quiet, quiet enough for front line use. Lear Jet has been working on a virtually pollution-free steam engine for motor vehicles. HEW's National Air Pollution Control Administration is subsidizing the design of a 100-hp steam-powered system to propel a six-passenger car at 75 mph.

Some hope for quieting larger vehicles may exist in the $300,-000 grant awarded by the Department of Transportation to the

* The source of electric power for New York City.

Dallas Transit System to test buses driven by a non-polluting Freon-powered *external* combustion engine. In 1968 I rode in an experimental bus being developed at GM. Operated by a gas-turbine engine, it emitted a very low over-all noise level. If the distinct and unpleasant whine which is characteristic of these engines can be eliminated, the end result could be a comparative ear-kiss. This bus, the RTX, could be ready for production in 1972 if somebody came up with at least 3,000 orders. It is estimated that the bus will cost twice the $28,000 now paid for GM's anti-social diesel buses. In the meantime, New York City is checking out experimental battery-operated buses.

To go from the sublime, there are experimental electric and fuel-cell motorcycles. Union Carbide claims its prototype fuel-cell motorbike at 25 mph allows the spectator to hear no more than the low hum of the chain drive.

All of these vehicles ride on rubber tires. Since tire noise impedes effective motor vehicle legislation, it is promising that the National Bureau of Standards is looking into the problem of tire noise. This is somewhat more reassuring than the news that the Rubber Manufacturers Association is cooperating with GM and the Society of Automotive Engineers to develop a tire noise testing procedure. The cooperation of the Rubber Manufacturers Association has gone further than the donating of one tire for needed research: the RMA has furnished several dozen.

If one seeks hard enough, one can find what could be the seeds for future noise abatement growth, or at least evidence that some areas of government can hear what's going on. On April 16, 1969, the Associated Press carried the information that the Birmingham, Alabama, city council had adopted a law making it illegal to operate transistor radios on city buses. It seems that the bus *drivers* had complained they were a distraction and kept them from hearing emergency sirens.

New York's Mayor Lindsay refused to permit six-second commercials to be blasted at subway riders at each station stop, callling the idea an invasion of privacy that could not be justified as revenue.

One of the more promising developments, for riders of mass transit, is the Bay Area Rapid Transit System now under construction in the San Francisco Bay area. Scheduled for completion in 1972, it is being built according to specifications that have certainly heretofore been alien to American mass transit purchases. The specifications section entitled *Audible Noise Control Requirements* starts out with this directive: "The Supplier shall devote particular attention to the design of quiet equipment, and methods shall be incorporated in the BART transit vehicle design to attenuate that equipment noise which does not meet the noise level limitations indicated."

There is a great deal of interest in the first "urban zone of quiet" created in the United States. This area is New York City's Central Park, where—thanks to the innovation of former Parks Commissioner Thomas P. F. Hoving—weekend motor traffic is banned. It would be more promising if the ban extended vertically to include aircraft flyovers.

New Bedford, Mass., Director of Public Health, Alphege Landreville, told a panel on public health at the University of Massachusetts: "Somehow, local health departments must accept new responsibilities in medical care . . . and what is now rapidly coming to the forefront, abatement of noise." He mentioned the wailing sirens of fire apparatus, ambulances, and police vehicles: "These are heard at all hours of the day and night and are particularly disturbing, irritating and frightening to young children who are awakened out of a sound sleep."

Politicans, many tending to abjure leadership in favor of waiting for evidence of public demand, are sensing their constituents' concern about the nitty-gritty of day-to-day living as well as the traditional major issues. In analyzing why Mayor Lindsay lost the Republican Primary in 1969, *The New York Times* reported that the major issues of crime in the streets and racial tension were not the only important factors. "Some more important factors would seem to be: . . . general frustration with the mundane urban crises of garbage cans, broken park benches, potholes . . . . " In short, the environment.

Not all politicians fully respect the noise issue, though they may anticipate votes in it. One candidate for state assembly lumped together as a platform plank: "elimination of air pollution, vagrancy, noise and parking problems." But maybe other candidates will keep alive the "Sweet Sunday" concept espoused by novelist Norman Mailer and newspaper columnist Jimmy Breslin when they ran for Mayor and President of New York City's City Council in the 1969 primary elections. Directed at air pollution, it would have required the ban of all vehicle traffic and pollution-causing machinery one Sunday a month.

Indicative of a growing Federal interest in noise abatement is the issuance of a contract by the U. S. Department of Housing and Urban Development for new and low-cost methods and materials to cut down noise transmission within dwellings and the entrance of noise into dwellings from the outdoors. The objective is laudable, but how much new building design and construction techniques will the $160,000 grant buy?

In 1966 President Johnson challenged planners and city officials to discover why the quality of life bore no relationship to our national affluence. Two years later, at the 1968 meeting of the American Institute of Planners, the delegates could put on a set of headphones and hear a variety of disagreeable city noises played at their actual sound levels. Perhaps it occurred to them that these noises are harming the quality of city life. Perhaps they returned to their respective cities reflecting on their personal reactions to these unpleasant sounds, and related them to proposals for center-city helicopters, STOLcraft, and multiple dwelling sites next to runways and adjacent to major highways. Perhaps.

Their colleagues overseas seem to dig noise abatement. One of the most interesting developments in new-town planning is the proposed community of Woolwich-Erith to be built in a three-mile stretch of marshy area on the Thames outside of London. Sponsored by the Greater London Council with the cooperation of two other London boroughs, it is a local government project designed to meet the needs of Londoners well into the next century. Needs will include an environment protected from noise, especially traffic noise.

In this new community, traffic will be concentrated on a few main distributor roads designed to assure free-flow circulation to eliminate stop-and-go noises. To protect the community from the through road there will be an embankment on either side, and a 300-foot play area strip will be between the embankment and the first row of houses. The local distributor road will be flanked on one side by a continuous row of dwellings designed so that their living rooms face away from the noise source and toward the quiet housing areas and the sun. In this way the noise on the inner face of the buildings can be reduced as much as four times. Where the local distributor road is between the sun and the homes, a non-residential barrier building will be erected.

Expressways through cities need not be a new source of noise. The Philadelphia City Council fought the plan for an open ditch road from Independence Hall to the Delaware River. In a cooperative venture between the Bureau of Public Roads, the Department of Housing and Urban Development, Interior, and the Pennsylvania Highway Department, a landscaped cover *may* be built over the road.

It is promising that some in government circles believe pollution should be made uneconomical. There should not be a "right to pollute." President Johnson's Science Advisory Committee had recommended in a report that a careful study be made of tax-like systems under which all polluters would be subject to "effluent charges" in proportion to their contribution to pollution.

Another method of adding to the cost of making noise is the "amenity" grants concept, whereby people made to suffer excessive noise through no fault of their own are given some assistance in barricading their homes. The British started this concept by enabling noise-stricken householders living within 12 miles of Heathrow Airport to receive up to half the cost of soundproofing a maximum of three rooms.

A Los Angeles proposal asks that there be a $1 anti-noise use tax on each passenger and ton of cargo using the airport. The money would be used to finance soundproofing of homes, schools, and church structures in zones of high airport noise levels. There is some uncertainty about the right of a municipality to tax interstate commerce. A precedent-shattering lawsuit is being instigated by the affected Los Angeles School District against the City Department of Airports. If undertaken, this suit will answer the key question: can one government agency enjoy the right to cause another to spend large sums of money solving a problem caused by the first agency.

This fight has won the support of the Los Angeles *Times*, which editorialized that the airport should include as part of the cost of doing business the cost of keeping the community habitable. If the schools win this type of case, one could look forward, perhaps, to suits against the FAA to compensate for the soundproofing of the Kennedy Center in Washington, as well as to suits against airports nationwide to help pay the cost of decibel retreat.

Noise abatement conferences sponsored by public-oriented groups are becoming available for the education of private and public officials. In Europe, representatives of the construction industry, as well as a broad spectrum of public officials, attended a conference sponsored by the Austrian Federation for Noise Abatement. Instead of being indoctrinated to disregard the complaints of noise victims as neurotic behavior, they were told that the noise offenders may be having mental difficulties and be in need of psychiatric help! This was a refreshing switch.Instead of belaboring the difficulties of enforcing anti-noise law, the delegates were given the benefit of the experience of the Zurich noise control office. Instead of listening to diatribes against noise control regulations, engineers discussed the need for expanded city ordinances and more enforcement. While American building department officials had yet to include noise insulation in their area of responsibility, the Chief Buildings Commissioner of Vienna was describing the improvements in his regulations for the planning and construction of buildings.

When public officials—and private contractors—leave this type of meeting, they are equipped to cope with the specifics of noise abatement. What is more important, they leave imbued with a sense of common purpose—protection of the public.

From Honolulu to Anchorage, Alaska, from Seattle to Oregon to Los Angeles to Pittsburgh, Chicago and New York, one hears of signs of demand for an end to the tyranny of noise.

As this book was being written, there were signs that the governmental indifference to the noise issue was beginning to change. It is beginning to dawn upon our law makers and our administrators that the public's noise complaints are valid and must be faced.

Some local governments are beginning to recognize the need for noise abatement agencies; a few state governments are moving to develop comprehensive noise abatement programs. On a national level, we now see an Office of Noise Abatement in the Department of Transportation, an Office of Noise Abatement Research and Technology in the Department of Housing and Urban Development, and another attempt, this time spearheaded by Senator Muskie, to give the Department of Health, Education and Welfare a noise abatement function.

The Nixon administration has recognized noise pollution in the Cabinet-level Environmental Quality Council, and a Council on Environmental Quality in the Executive Office of the President. President Nixon is seeking to place all pollution problems in one environmental protection administration. The Congress was waiting for the report of a Presidential Task Force which would spell out the specific agency to be responsible for environmental matters, noise included.

The Congress itself is developing a body of environment-oriented senators and congressmen, among them a handful aware that noise, too, is a factor in environmental deterioration. Among the friends of noise abatement are Senators Hatfield, Hart, Randolph, Muskie, and Nelson, and Representatives Lowenstein, Ottinger, Ryan, and Reuss.

Noise abatement is bound to benefit from the spin-off from the Environmental Teach-In of 1970.

The ferment described in this chapter is no guarantee of the needed commitment to abate. The majority still fails to understand the need to lessen the noise assault, and among the enlightened who acknowledge "noise pollution" one finds a tendency to relegate its solution to the bottom of the heap of pressing problems. Too many fail to understand that today's technological and congestion-instigated problems cannot be treated sequentially: air pollution first, water pollution second, noise last, etc. Technology and congestion won't wait; if we are to survive we must attack these problems on all fronts at the same time. We have no choice.

CHAPTER TEN

It's Up To All Of Us

You are more often than not on your own in this noisy world.
As a would-not-be noise receiver you can try to avoid noisy
places, and try to shield your immediate environment from external noise sources. You can try to keep down the noise produced in your own home. You can simulate partial deafness by
putting things in or over your ears. You can make noise to drown
out other noises. And, if all else fails, you can always flee—
perhaps even to a quieter spot.

Whenever you might move, you can check for present and
future noise-annoyance sources (it won't be easy):

Local, state, and Federal agencies can be queried for current
paths of surface, air, and underground transportation. You can
check on contemplated road and subway construction, emergency holding patterns, new flight paths for jets and helicopters,
new STOLport flight paths, and proposed hovercraft routes. You
may even be able to obtain noise contour maps from the respon-

sible agency (if any) and try to get an interpretation of what these various transportation intrusions will mean in terms of known criteria for hearing loss, speech and sleep interference, and annoyance.

Be sure to ask for flight paths under both visual and instrument rules. (Instrument flight may be permitted over your head.) Find out if there are any limitations on aviation in terms of morning starting time limits, and restrictions on evening and Sunday morning flights. If there are no adequate restrictions, and there is no choice of dwelling, make provision with friends or relatives for an occasional restorative weekend sleep-over visit.

Check the distance to the nearest through road. Is it heavily trafficked? What is the percentage of truck traffic? Is it smooth-flow, or is there a stoplight or intersection that spells horn honking, brake squeal, and acceleration roar? Avoid living near a grade, or expect the noise of grinding gears. If there is a parking lot or public garage nearby, does the community exercise any noise control regulations over it? Do the police enforce or ignore them?

Check for future lengthy public works and utility projects, such as new sewers, water mains, underground gas and electric lines, telephone conduits, and so forth.

Prepare a "siren index." Locate the nearest fire and police stations and hospitals. If statistics are available, study the number and localities of fires, crimes, and accidents, and project when and how often siren wails can be expected.

If the site of the dwelling you are investigating is near a river, how do you feel about boat and fog horns? Double-check on present and future plans to use this artery as a flight path for helicopters, STOLs, hovercraft, and hydrofoils.

Check the distance from schools and playgrounds, coffee-houses, nightclubs, bars, and other sources of potentially raucous noise.

Check for proximity to churches and synagogues. Are chimes amplified? What is their schedule? Has central air conditioning been installed, and if so, has it been silenced? Religious activities are generally exempt from noise control regulations, and there have been reported cases where religious administrators have refused to abate mechanical noise nuisance emanating from their premises.

Use your ingenuity to detect or predict other noise sources that could become a problem. It is much easier to *avoid* noise nuisance by not locating near it, than to get rid of it or to ward it off after you have moved in.

So much for the site. Now for the dwelling itself.

The homeowner who builds to his own specifications can ask for sound-conditioned construction. If he buys a home already built, his problems are similar to those of tenants in a multiple-dwelling unit.

Assuming the dwelling site is acceptable, try to avoid renting an apartment that is subject to undue noise stress because of either interior noise sources or poor isolation from adjacent apartments and service equipment.

Think twice before paying a higher rent to be on a high floor. According to studies made for the Greater London Council, height in itself is not a major factor in reducing average noise levels on either dwellings or office buildings. Exposure to other noise sources in the line of sight may in some circumstances *increase* the noise level on upper floors. For example, the upper floors may experience aviation noises from which the lower floors are shielded.

Look for an apartment in which at least the bedroom faces the rear of the building and is thus removed from the front line of street noise. As much as a 15-decibel difference may exist between the front and back of a building—assuming the rear apartment's rooms are not above a kitchen, under a flight path, or near an unsilenced exhaust fan or air conditioner. Courtyards are not necessarily quieter, either.

Is the apartment near garage doors? If it is to be your own garage, nylon guides or runners can be installed. If it is a large garage for transient parkers who are invited to honk their horns as the open sesame, inquire about local horn ordinances that may make this an illegal act.

Look for instances of concern about sound control. Are the front doors tight-fitting to screen out hallway noises? Or too short for their frames, indicating that the builder tried to save money by making the common hallway part of the central ventilating system? Don't accept casual statements about good sound insulation. Ask to see the actual wall and floor specifications and field-test results. If you can, ask an architect or acoustical consultant to analyze their adequacy for you. *Caveat emptor* is the byword for securing a quiet apartment.

Some experienced apartment hunters bring a friend or two with them and try to get them into the adjacent apartment or the one above, where they play a radio, drag a chair across the floor, walk about, jump a couple of times, talk loudly, and observe if the apartment overhead is carpeted, especially the bedroom. It is also wise to see whether appliances are mounted on the common wall.

It is a good idea to try to visit a prospective apartment when the neighbors are home, in the evening or during the weekend.

As you go about the building, check for potential noise from elevator doors and motors and ventilating and air conditioning compressors and blowers.

Within the apartment, scout around. Is shower noise contained within the bathroom? Can you hear neighboring bathroom activity? Is the ventilator in the bathroom sound-conditioned, or does it serve as a two-way megaphone? Are doors between rooms tight? Undercut doors make it difficult to isolate noises made by individual family members. Are the light switches the noiseless type, or do they operate with a click that can shock a nervous system under stress?

Turn on all the "mechanized conveniences" at the same time: dishwasher, garbage disposal unit, range exhaust, and air conditioners. Mentally, add the noise of your own appliances: blender, vacuum, electric can opener, dryer. Will they be isolated from other rooms by solid walls and tight door construction? Imagine listening to your stereo or television while the kitchen appliances are working and the children are playing in their room. Imagine also possible external noises: traffic, aviation, sirens, construction. The total of this is called "maximum acoustical stress," and is of course only theoretical. But unfortunately, most apartments in America would not pass these tests.

Do not chastise yourself if you move into a noise trap despite your attempts to avoid one. Even noise experts get stung. One unfortunate checked his $500-a-month apartment while the building was still under construction, and was satisfied it would be quiet. Once he moved in, he became painfully aware of the heating and air conditioning system directly below his apartment. Only the threat of legal action forced the landlord to install vibration-insulators on the noisy pumps and motors.

If one has the misfortune of leasing a noisy apartment, then what?

The main ingress for exterior noise of traffic is the window. If we could forego visual contact with the outside world, the simplest noise solution would be to seal the windows—ideally with lead or leaded sheets, less effectively, with plywood. Well, one *can* live without outdoor light or view, but not without fresh air.

Sound-trapped ventilating units, with and without air conditioning, are available. Heavier window panes or commercial double-hung windows are another solution. An inexpensive but relatively effective method is to use tight-fitting storm windows, with neoprene beads if possible. The ventilation problem can be overcome by having the regular window and the storm window open at opposite ends. Remember this acoustic rule of thumb: if a sound wave makes a 45° or greater bend, some of its energy is lost.

Even if you cannot do much about the windows, some of the

reverberation from outside noise can be reduced by covering the ceiling and walls with sound-absorbers. Acoustical ceiling tile is available and can also be applied to walls. Acoustical tile minimizes the annoyance of *reflected* sound. It is not a sound barrier. It is not a noise insulator. (Unknowing or unscrupulous contractors and dealers will sell acoustical tile to noise victims who are seeking relief from impact noises generated by upstairs neighbors. The product is not designed for this purpose, and sales made under these circumstances verge on fraud.) The product itself must be an effective sound absorber, with a minimal thickness as well as absorbent properties. "Acoustical paint" has no significant sound-absorption properties. Check with the Acoustical and Insulating Materials Association for a list of standard absorption coefficients.

Walls can be covered with soft drapes, tapestries, or wall hangings; our castle-dwelling ancestors knew a thing or two about echo control.

Furnish the apartment with upholstered furniture and line the walls with books, both of which absorb sound. If possible, make the "party wall" your bookshelf wall. Or perhaps you can add closets to this wall. If so, keep linen, clothing, and other absorbers in them. For acute problems, a false wall can be added.

Noises coming through a wall adjacent to a neighboring apartment can be a pernicious problem. Sound-absorbing treatment *will not* keep out this kind of intrusion.

The Noise Abatement Society suggests "fibre insulating board mounted on wooden battens for reducing airborne noises between rooms, such as baby cries and voices." Musicians often treat their practice rooms in this way. Ideally, this type of installation should be made by an acoustical building contractor.

Study your lease, and know what violates its nondisturbance clauses.

Establish contact with your neighbor. Inquire if his television and hi fi could be placed away from the party wall. Try to make an agreement that each of you will keep the volume at a reasonable level, and not emphasize the bass (sound-insulated walls are more effective in keeping out the upper frequencies than the lower ones). Perhaps all tenants can get together and agree to remove their shoes upon entering their apartments, Japanese style. Check your lease for a carpeting clause.

One readily corrected source of impact noise is that created at the interface of a metal ceiling fixture and the ceiling. If this is a problem, have a rubber gasket installed.

Because acoustical slums are to be with us for many decades, and the use of amplified sound sources is proliferating, acoustic consideration dictates the use of headphones as a desired control technique. Their use not only keeps you from annoying neighbors, especially late at night, it improves the enjoyment of listening by screening out the "normal" intrusive sounds that keep one from hearing soft music and the nuances which heighten the sense of "presence." Convince your neighbor of this.

Variety tells us: "Headphones make it possible for a musician to practice an amplified instrument without creating hostile neighbors." Remember this when your community wants to improve its anti-noise laws.

If you become desperate, explore "personal protection," the euphemism for inducing voluntary partial deafness by means of ear protectors.

The most common device is the earplug, recommended if one has trouble hearing acoustic signals, if vocational noise exposure warrants ear protection, and if local noise is extremely irritating. Originally designed to minimize the danger of industrial and military hearing loss, it has been claimed that more than 18 million Americans wear earplugs on the street and in bed. Manufacturers throughout the world are producing earplugs that are hard, soft, or malleable. England's KIFA, which is like a tampon, comes complete with a tassel for removal. Another company has

Muffles. A Swedish variety is the glass-wool Billesholm Horsel-Skydd (*mott buljer*), which is sold in English-speaking countries as Billesholm's Anti Noise. In Germany one finds Ohreschutzer. In the United States, Flents and Nods are examples of the malleable (wax) type of earplug. Although most earplugs are sold directly to industry, some varieties can be purchased in local drugstores.

Besides some physical discomfort and inconvenience, earplugs are expensive. What do plastic earplugs cost individuals who buy them for non-factory wear? A whopping $1.50, at least. Industry and the military, accounting for a substantial amount of the sales, buy them in quantities of 500 pairs or more at a time, and may pay as little as 75¢ per pair.

The acoustic earmuff is somewhat more comfortable than the earplug, because the cup covers the ear and the pressure is on the side of the surface of the head rather than in the ear itself. Earmuffs, if ordered in large numbers, can be found at something like $5. At this low, low price, one researcher estimated it would cost industry something like between $27.5 and $89.1 million per year to substitute ear protection for noise reduction. This estimate is based on the assumption that there are 34 million workers in noisy jobs, and that all must be protected from above-damage-risk noise exposure.

Since I had to buy at retail, my sundry collection of earplugs and two pairs of earmuffs cost me about $50. The irony is that not only does the non-occupational public have to pay the higher retail prices, it receives less value, because both plugs and muffs are designed to protect from hearing loss, and not from annoyance. The annoyance is reduced; it is not reduced enough.

Earplugs do not provide good protection from the sound energy of lower frequencies, and the rumble of traffic noise is most often of low frequency. Although the whine of the jet compressor is high frequency, the bulk of jet-engine noise is also in the lower frequencies. Nevertheless, for a modicum of relief, earplugs are almost mandatory for individuals living near airports.

Check with your doctor before wearing earplugs. I wore half-a-dozen varieties during the siege of upper Sixth Avenue, until my ear doctor told me not to, that I was irritating my ear canal. Earplugs must be carefully fitted: the two human ears differ in size. The Public Health Service recommends that earplugs for industrial use be issued only by a plant physician (or nurse) who is qualified to select the proper plug, as well as instruct the user on how wear and care for these devices. The agency further recommends that earplug users be spot-checked to insure that these safeguards are being correctly employed.

Caution: do not use the type of earplug that has a metal valve, which is supposed to stay open in low-noise situations to allow conversation. The metal valve represents a potential hazard if one receives a blow on the head.

Solid earplugs require care. The softer the device, the more comfortable it is to use; however, the soft ones are less durable. Ear wax, dirt, perspiration, and other foreign matter can cause the plugs' resilient constituents to harden, crack, or expand, and become too soft. On the other hand, harder plugs, although more durable, are less comfortable and more likely to irritate the ear canal. Travelers should be aware that earplugs are especially likely to cause ear canal inflammation in tropical climates.

Cotton is worthless as an earplug.

One other precaution: do not wear earplugs while brushing your teeth; the effect is not unlike chalk rasping over a blackboard.

Paradoxically, earplugs make it more difficult to hear speech in quieter surroundings than in noisier ones, such as a factory. Speech comprehension is difficult in areas of low background noise if one is wearing earplugs. Worn while sleeping, earplugs could muffle a child's weak nighttime call, some sounds of danger, and other "noises" that one wants to receive.

After years of educational programs to promote hearing conservation, factory workers continue to resist protecting their ears
with earplugs. Apparently the certainty of discomfort overrules
the threat of deafness. These earplug resisters must also know
from experience that, in some intense noise situations, plugs
afford little or no relief or protection.

Developed by the military to protect "aircraft guiders" on
carrier decks from hearing loss, acoustic earmuffs are minimally
effective in screening out the annoying lower-frequencies of everyday noises.

Any effectiveness of muffs that are available for general use
must be weighed against these devices' shortcomings. There is
the discomfort from perspiration that develops between the
muffs' tight seal and the side of the head. Their use makes tele-
phoning a comical operation. It is quite a feat to clamp one of
the cups over the telephone receiver and keep one's eyeglasses
from falling off, while trying to hold a pen! (Wearers of glasses
who are subject to a "temporary" spell of construction noise
might consider obtaining contact lenses.) Because of their pro-
truding cups, earmuffs cannot be used while sleeping. They interfere with lovemaking, and a careless passionate kiss between two
persons wearing earmuffs could leave one partner with a mouth
full of plastic or a black eye.

To appeal to women, manufacturers have developed a model
earmuff that has a rotating band that can be worn under the chin,
leaving coiffures unscathed. Earmuff manufacturers are also getting away from the drab gray of their initial product, and offering
models in orange and blue.

Your hands are the most natural form of ear protection. At the
Human Engineering Laboratories of the U.S. Army, a study was
conducted of the comparative effectiveness of fingers, palms,
tragi (the prominence in front of the external opening of the ear),
and earplugs as noise blockers. The tragi won, hands down—or
up, rather. At 34 decibels attenuation, the tragi were found to be
quite superior to earplugs, which averaged only 21 decibels at-

tenuation. Moderately effective were fingers for attenuating low-frequency sounds, and palms for high frequencies.

These findings would suggest that tragi should be drepressed over the ear canals for jet flyovers, fingers stuck in the canals for traffic noise, and the palms of one's hands placed over the canals for construction noise. Earplugs and earmuffs have the advantage of leaving one's hands free, however. Perhaps Mother Nature will respond to the plight of modern urban man, and create a mutant with self-closing tragi.

One serious threat of intense noise is that sound energy can penetrate the soft tissues of the body. To protect particularly vulnerable flight-deck personnel, a British manufacturer has developed an anti-noise suit. Resembling a suit of chain mail, it covers one from the top of the head to the bottom of the torso.

If your noise is not intense enough to penetrate your abdomen or groin, you may be satisfied with the completely enclosed acoustic helmet developed for spaceship launching. Equipped with its own oxygen supply, telephone jacks, and built-in radio transmitter/receiver, it makes possible communication with one's loved ones, while at the same time solving the air pollution problem.

To be forced to wear ear protectors is like being forced to wear an oxygen mask as the answer to air pollution. This price lessens the life experience. After reviewing the complexities and inadequacies of trying to avoid noise, it makes more sense to reduce noise at the source. We must design for quiet.

But it should be clear by now that a quieter world is up to all of us. Government and industry cannot and will not respond without incentives. Government and industry certainly will not respond if they believe that the demand for less noise is only the feeble outcry of a few hypersensitive "kooks," or "chronic malcontents."

Years of exposure and frustration may have deadened your

awareness. Prepare for your attack by forcing yourself to listen. Make up your own list of disturbing noises; or, start with that list of ten most unwanted sounds of 1956:

1. Refuse collection	6. Unmuffled exhausts
2. Hornblowing	7. Street repairs
3. Acceleration of motors	8. Sound trucks
4. Blaring of radio and TV sets	9. Construction riveting
5. Aircraft noise	10. Doormen's whistles

How many of these sources are you exposed to today? Which new ones would you add to the list? In what order?

Keep a noise diary. List sources, time of day, how you reacted. Were you distracted, conversation halted, sleep lost? How do others react? Next time you visit a hospital, notice whether your friend or relative is shielded from the sounds of other patients and of hospital procedures. Can he really rest?

Visit a school. Does it have an amplified intercom with a shrill speaker? Tiled hall acting like an echo chamber? Noisy lunch-room?

Contrast your regular acoustic environment with the sounds of a natural environment. Can you hear the sounds of birds, murmuring of water, rustling of wind in the trees?

Has noise made your home a place to escape from? How often do you leave your community, not because you want to, but because escape from noise is a necessity? How much additional are you paying to find a quiet vacation spot? Can you find one?

These acts of conscious listening will force you to question the price of progress. You will develop a tangible, albeit ugly, picture of how uncaring people have been permitted to degrade your environment.

The acute awareness of excessive noise may temporarily make you ill, but this should only strengthen your resolve to act. To learn to hear noises is not to learn to love them. Convert your hurt, or that of other noise victims, into curiosity, your curiosity into anger, and your anger into action.

In addition to learning to identify the noises, learn to identify the justifications for noise. Since the dawn of history myths have been used to keep an oppressed group from asking too many questions. Myths are seldom challenged, especially today, when they are created and dispensed by high priests as awesome as physicians, scientists, and engineers.

To spot justifications for noise, watch for the following myths: Noise is the price of progress. Noise is a necessary evil. Noise abatement must be realistic (that is, not cost anything). The public does not want to pay for quiet. Silencing will hurt progress. Background noise is acceptable; it is the intrusive noise that is the problem. Daytime noise is more acceptable than nighttime noise.

(On that last, the Wilson Committee reported evidence that the total annoyance caused to the population is roughly the same by day and by night, and concluded that "a great noise in a residential area will be most disturbing during the night, and in commercial areas . . . probably during the day.")

Hold suspect "acceptability" goals. Who is behind them? Industry? Government agencies that use industry's definitions of what your acoustic environment is to be like? Is "acceptability" defined as a comfortable environment, or one to be endured?

In any tyranny—and that of noise is no different—the problem is to keep alive the flicker of hope. This can be done by making noise visible. One technique is to develop your own set of "noise games." For example, play Community Noise Protection Index. Make up a list of the ideal elements you would like in a noise ordinance. Research your local, state, and Federal laws. Then prepare the score card:

ORDINANCE, REGULATION, OR LAW

NOISE SOURCE	None	Meaningful	Not Meaningful	Enforced	Not Enforced
TRANSPORTATION *Surface* Decibel limits Horn use Tire treads Emergency vehicle sirens					
Air Heliports STOLports Jetports Aerial corridors					
MOBILE FACTORIES Garbage trucks Fuel and other "accessory function" trucks					
BUILDING CODE Insulation standards Noise isolation by design					
CONSTRUCTION Hours of operation Equipment silencing Decibel limit at property line					
BARS, NIGHTCLUBS					

ORDINANCE, REGULATION, OR LAW

NOISE SOURCE	None	Meaningful	Not Meaningful	Enforced	Not Enforced
PLANNING					
Zoning decibel and design standards					
Traffic flow					
Residence protected from aviation					
TRANSISTOR RADIOS IN PUBLIC PLACES					
NOISE CONTROL ENFORCEMENT AGENCY					
NOISE CONTROL LABORATORY					
NOISE ABATEMENT COURSES					
High school					
College (undergraduate)					
Required for engineers					

You may be told that cost is the reason your community does not have much in the way of enforcement. So now compute the "cost" of noise. For example, count the number of air compressor and jackhammer operators employed in your community, establish your own idea of the dollar value of the ability to hear speech, and multiply. Establish an arbitrary value for the efficiency lost because of poor sleep, and estimate how many in your community are not getting a good night's sleep because of sirens, unmuffled noises of social utility, and the like. Set a dollar value on a businessman's day, and deduct the percentage lost because of disturbed sleep, masked speech, and other distractions.

Play "shoulds." What could and should be done, and how, and by whom?

The act of paying attention to noise will elevate you to a role of leadership. Organize a noise-defense unit in your community. Power structures tend to respond more readily to group pressure. An organization also facilitates the development of strategy and tactics, and the opening of lines of communication.

Do not be deterred from organizing because there may be a government noise abatement function, or a government task force on noise. Government represents all interests equally—but the vested interests more equally than the public's.

If funds are a problem and overhead must be kept to a minimum, it might be worth while to activate a noise abatement committee within an already existing organization. One advantage of this kind of affiliation is that your issue gains immediate entry into the body politic.

If funds will be available without having to offer a tax deductibility, forego that luxury and be free to lobby for necessary legislation.

Either way, raise funds for the task to be done. It is a myth that civic non-profit efforts must be amateurish and saddled with economic sacrifice. You are preparing for a knock-down, dragout fight, not the Olympics. Raise funds for the necessary office operations, for special skills, for advertising, publicity, research, and legal battles. Travel funds will make possible attendance at the various noise abatement meetings now springing up; a speaker fund will bring noise abatement expertise to your own meeting.

Organize volunteers, the lifeblood of a grassroots movement. Now you are ready to think strategy and employ tactics. Look upon the fight for quiet as a chess game played against the indifferent. Plan to bypass the ineffectual pawns, harass the more powerful rooks, bishops, and knights, and ultimately checkmate the noisemaker king.

Do not be insular in your organizing activities. For example, seek to win the cooperation of the farmer and his wife—for the common purpose of environmental survival. The farmer can offer urban man Congressional support; a well-funded Department of Agriculture; direct aid through the extension services operated by the land-grant colleges and financed by the Federal government.

Go further, and seek an urban-suburban-rural coalition.

Place noise abatement on the agenda of a civic organization. Provide substantiating background material. Work up an antinoise resolution, and help win support for it.

A demonstration is a great convincer. When the late Lucy Milligan invited me to appear before the New York Federation of Women's Clubs, I plugged in a small electric motor mounted on a wooden base. It had the irritating whine of a vacuum cleaner. Then, like a magician, I made three successive moves. The whine disappeared and the motor was barely audible. Noise control expert Francis Kirschner had prepared a noise-control-in-practice kit for me to use. The noise disappeared with the insertion of makeshift mufflers.

"Now, ladies," I told the audience, "if anyone tells you noise is the price of progress, remember what you have just seen and heard." The resolution was passed with what I was told was an unusual unanimity.

Get the doctors involved. Don't let them get away with the customary "take an aspirin."

It is high time that the otologists—who have borne the brunt of the work in occupational and military noise—be augmented by neurologists, endocrinologists, psychiatrists—the entire spectrum of medicine. We must learn more about the extra-auditory effects of noise. If the evidence is not conclusive for a relationship between noise and disease, the epidemiologists must determine whether there is a greater chance for an ulcer or a heart attack in a noise-stressed environment. To persist in ignoring the total systemic response to noxious sound energy is as foolishly restrictive as to see air pollution only in terms of its effect on visibility.

Medical schools and other research institutions must try to discover why the living organism is annoyed by noise, must explore the significance of the physiological changes. They should be trying to find out why one person is more disturbed than another. They should also try to discover if—for cultural and other reasons—only a minority will *admit* to noise disturbance.

If nothing else, ask your physician if the concept of preventive medicine does not warrant his interest in abatement. Ask him whether or not he has heard of doctors who find it difficult to use stethoscopes in today's noisy world. Ask if he himself needs the new anti-noise stethoscope. Tell your doctor that his colleagues complain about noise just as much as you do. If you have an ailment for which he has prescribed rest, tranquility, adequate sleep, ask him what drugstore can fill that prescription.

Enlist the support of the church and the synagogue. Organized religion can do more than tell its congregations that noise is cruel, that noise violates the dignity of man. The houses of worship can practice what they preach by themselves being good neighbors.

In 1966 the Department of Commerce estimated that $1,-275,000 would be spent for religious buildings. Let the church or synagogue, in sending out construction bids, ask for quiet methods and materials, and award their bids to the contractor who offers to build quietly and for quiet. This action would hasten the end of the curse of construction noise. The religious institutions can ask their contractors and architects to install central air conditioning that is properly designed not to cause noise annoyance. And finally, they can check to make sure their chimes aren't a problem to the community.

End the alienation between the makers of things and the public that must live with them. It may be against the law for you to silence a noisemaker's machine; it is not against the law to talk to him about it.

Get to know the noisemaker and his experts. Make yourself and your neighbors visible to his distributors, his trade associations. Friendly intervisitation will create an image of the public as flesh and blood, and not stereotyped statistical abstractions.

What do you talk about at such meetings? Talk dollars and cents. Talk about noise-induced hearing loss and inefficiency, and ill-will. Offer incentives, and protection from unfair—that is, noisy—competition.

Explain to a contractor the hidden costs of potential workmen's compensation claims. Explain to a factory operator the possibilities of lowered productivity, higher accident rates. Explain to all noisemakers of commerce and industry the potential of lawsuits, not only for hearing loss, but for the destruction of environmental quality.

Be prepared to show evidence of a market for quieter products, and that you are urging private purchasers and city agencies to "buy quiet."

Offer an awards program that will engender goodwill for the provider of quiet.

With this type of rounded negotiations program, the dialogue between the public and the noisemaker can start on a basis of genuine desire for exploring mutual interests.

This dialogue is not meant to be a love-in. The noisemaker must be given to understand that you mean business—his business, if he does not respond. Use stockholder clout. Buy stock in corporations manufacturing noisy products. Encourage your friends to do the same. Then attend stockholders meetings and demand design for quiet. Conversely, refuse to own stock in companies that will not curb noise pollution.

Business thrives on competition, we are told. Stir up a little competition from less-polluting substitutes. It is not inconceivable that new space-age entrepreneurs will supplant the rigid old-guard that refuses to de-pollute its products.

Search the catalogues of foreign manufacturers, and encourage the importing of quieter products. Not until the discovery of quieter, competitively priced European construction equipment in 1966 were American manufacturers encouraged to lose their timidity and market some quiet products of their own.

More can be done than promoting the products of quiet design. Censure the noisy ones. Obtain the decibel readings of the noisy appliances and vehicles in your community, and publicize the results.

Economic pressure may encourage the American noisemaker to think of quiet as well as style. One method of protest is the boycott. Select one product that is noisier than others. If all products in that category are equally noisy, boycott all. This will entail sacrifice, but the noisemaker will not believe that noise is a bother until he sees evidence of some sacrifice in comfort, time or money. It should be possible to boycott one airline of several serving a given city. A leaf can be taken from the conservation movement: the Maine State Biologists Association conducted a national boycott of the products of a company accused of polluting a stream with its potato processing plant, according to *The New York Times* (April 6, 1969).

If industry cannot or will not design for quiet, the public may have to change its life-style, and forego some of the convenience and speed purchases that help degrade the environment. We may have to return to the use of hand-operated appliances in place of machines.

Industry should take the initiative to design for quiet without waiting for legislation and proof of a market. The motivation is the preservation of the human environment.

In the United States we are still waiting for the necessary

legislation. The pitifully few ordinances wither for lack of enforcement. First and foremost we need to develop a climate for noise abatement. If we succeed in doing this, pressure for enforcement will be as child's play.

It is not enough to build a better mouse trap; it must be promoted. It is not enough for the noise victims and the enlightened to know the dangers of unregulated noise. Noise must be made visible. As the Europeans told me, if people could see decibels, silence would be the order of the day.

It is not easy to convey an image of noise which will move the public to demand abatement. Fishermen get upset if a lake is polluted; the housewife can see soot and relate pollution to her laundry bill; chemical pollution is understandable to most. But noise is an abstraction, its noxious qualities difficult to demonstrate. Set against the conveniences and symbols of progress, arguments of environmental and personal degradation appear puny, at first. Education on behalf of noise abatement must be given top priority.

A simple technique, but of far-reaching value, is to ask your local radio and TV stations to broadcast volume-turndown messages after 11:00 p.m. As a matter of fact, try to get nighttime announcers to promote sleep-protection from whatever source.

Coordinate your anti-noise campaigns with an enforcement drive. Arouse the public to support anti-noise regulations. The AICB encourages its member organizations to conduct national anti-noise campaigns. Such noise abatement weeks, sponsored in cooperation with government, have taken place in Copenhagen, Rome, and Cordoba, Argentina, to name a few of the major cities. As part of such programs, the French noise abatement group has awarded Palms of Silence to government officials who have undertaken noise abatement actions. Austria has an annual "Noise-free Week."

Success will vary, depending upon the goals, the preparation, and the cooperation. Cordoba (population 600,000) has a staff of five men trained in the city university's acoustic laboratory.

Although its first "Silence Week" brought only temporary relief, it did lay the groundwork for the eventual development of Argentina's first Noise Abatement Council, as well as improvements in municipal anti-noise regulations.

All things being equal, it is better to show than to tell. At Baden-Baden, delegates were taken on a tour of the "Quiet Zone," the largest such within a city. This was followed by a demonstration of silenced and non-silenced equipment. Hearing is believing.

Interconnect the areas of noise stress. Never forget that unlike the other "pollutants" noise hits people in small pockets. Individuals in one building may vary in their awareness of a noise problem emanating from the street outside, or even from a given neighbor. The people in center-city or quiet suburbs may be indifferent to the lot of the people living near jetports. The people living near jetports not only are indifferent to center-city residents, they would want them to install STOLports and heliports, anything to reduce the hellish noise exposure near the airports. Educational programs must be designed to reach out to this disconnected noise-stressed population.

Do not be afraid to use humor: the public is becoming enured to tales of unrelieved suffering. Britain's John Connell, a public relations man by profession, encourages a wry statement of the problem, and the press responds. One of my favorite cartoons, published in *Punch*, depicts a suicide hurtling down a tall building, screaming at the top of his lungs. However, he is a considerate soul at heart, and as he passes the third-floor window of the Noise Abatement Society he dutifully muffles his screams, opening up fortissimo for the balance of the trip.

Sponsor meetings, symposia, and conferences. Locate specialists in medicine, engineering, and the humanities who have something constructive to say about noise abatement.

One suggestion for making noise visible is associated with something I saw in Copenhagen shortly after the end of its occupation by the Nazis. There were no signs of torture and executions. None, except that scattered through the city were small evergreen crosses, marking the sites where some patriotic Dane had paid the price of Hitler's progress.

To alert the public to the needless suffering and the hazards of the tyranny of noise, symbols should be erected at each construction site, in each neighborhood under air assault, in front of each dwelling impacted by neighboring air conditioning systems or noisy neighbors.

If education fails to win either improved product design, or legislation, the next step is direct protest. This is called Complaining.

The public often asks whether or not it is worthwhile to complain. The answer is an absolute yes. Complaints are a significant indicator to the noisemaker. Though complaints can be manipulated, can be made to show an increase or decrease for the same noise source, the sophisticated noisemaker knows that individual reactions are potential threats. Noise control experts tell noisemakers to watch for the following community behavior: a letter of complaint to officials, a telephone call to the operator of the noise source, or the initiation of legal action to suppress the noise-producing activity. How far an individual or the community will go, is a barometer of how much noise the receiver will take. It is therefore important to register some form of protest when faced with a serious noise problem. Students of Queen Elizabeth College in Kensington, England, reacted militantly, but without violence, when construction noise kept them from studying for their exams; they simply went on strike.

It is difficult to assess complaints as a noise indicator, because the lack of complaints may have little to do with the seriousness of the noise in question. Lack of complaints may merely mean a lack of leadership, or a lack of the ability to communicate with the noisemaker or government. A lack of complaint may also be the result of individuals' attitudes toward complaining.

The complexity of complaints as a means of evaluating a noise problem was noted in the Oklahoma City sonic boom tests, where the number of complaints was high, but the statistical percentage low. An evaluation of the complaint level was made in a government report on the tests:

"This relatively low complaint level at Oklahoma City was due primarily to three factors. First, there was widespread ignorance about where to complain; 70 per cent of all respondents expressed such ignorance in the interview. Second, there was a general feeling of futility in the usefulness of complaining; only 4 per cent felt there was a 'very good' chance of doing something about the booms, and another 10 per cent felt there was even a 'good' chance to do something. Third, the general pattern of complaining about local problems was low in Oklahoma City; only about a fourth of all people felt like complaining about a serious local problem when they had one.

"Only one in every twelve annoyed persons actually expressed their feelings to the FAA complaint center."

Don't complain in generalities. Know your target: be specific. Develop a "noise intrusion profile." What is causing the noise? At what time of day? Who owns the source? Who operates it? Any regulations violated? In the case of aviation noise, plane spotters should have detailed data on type of plane, time of day, identification number, distance above buildings, and so forth.

Try to be specific about the impact of that noise source. What kind of structures are being hit: homes, hospitals, schools, churches? How many elderly, how many children? If schools are near an airport, how much classroom time is lost? One town effectively organized to stop a proposed private airport by producing evidence of how the resulting noise would impair classroom instruction. A state legislative committee was visibly impressed by a presentation which showed what the noise levels would be at the various schools and how this would interfere with speech communication.

Petitions—most effective if notarized—can provide useful statistics when taking a neighbor-noise complaint to court. Make sure that the press receives a copy of any letters of protest or petitions sent to government officials and/or noisemakers.

It is an art in itself to know where to complain and what government agency to complain to. Here is a partial list for New York City, just as one example:

Noise Source	Agency
Over-all	Central Complaint Bureau Environmental Protection Administration
Moving buses	Metropolitan Transportation Authority
Idling buses and trucks	Department of Air Pollution Control
Building construction (between 6:00 P.M. and 7:00 A.M. except with emergency permit)	Central Complaint Section, Buildings Department
Utility construction (between 11:00 P.M. and 7:00 A.M.)	Construction Division, Department of Water Supply, Gas and Electricity
Private garbage collection (between 11:00 P.M. and A.M.)	Trade Waste Division, Department of Licenses*
Public garbage collection	Sanitation Department
Helicopters	Noise Abatement Officer, Federal Aviation Administration
Jets taking off	Kennedy and LaGuardia Operations: Port of New York Authority

*For a cease and desist order, supply the name of the carting company and the time and date they were making the noise.

Noise Source	Agency
Jets landing	Noise Abatement Officer, Federal Aviation Administration
Noise from loudspeakers, sound trucks, and other electrically amplified devices	Police Department
Neighbors	
After 11:00 P.M.	Police Department
Before 11:00 P.M.	Your landlord
Restaurant air conditioners	Sanitary Inspection Office, Health Department

In addition to complaining to administrative and police agencies, by all means let your local, state, and Congressional legislators know what is going on. Your city councilman may be hearing the same noise you hear, but accepting it as the price of progress.

The legal attack should include those government agencies holding responsibility for protecting the health and safety of workers. Government officials should be sued for not moving to require reasonable and adequate protection for workers in extremely noisy factories and computerized offices. Work sites above 85 decibels should be prima facie evidence of neglect.

At some point the public must realize it has nothing to lose but its pains. Protest must become militant: non-violent, but persistent.

Petitions must be replaced with peaceful demonstrations. Professor Amitai Etzioni, a member of the President's National Commission on the Causes and Prevention of Violence, pointed out that many "respectable" members of the community were resorting to demonstrations as a political weapon: teachers, doctors, clergymen, and even police.

Picket to get attention. Picket the right targets. In the case of construction noise there is the contractor, the sponsoring developer or government agency, the manufacturer of the equipment, the manufacturer of the noisy components used to assemble that equipment. For good measure, picket City Hall and the medical societies.

Help the helpless. Picket construction and jet noise at hospitals and schools.

If desperate, try what others have tried: a noise for a noise. In England, citizens called Members of Parliament in the early hours of the morning to tell them they might be interested in knowing that there was jet noise in the land.

Check with your attorneys to clarify the legal aspects of this type of action. It is justified if in spite of the existence of silencing techniques the noisemaker continues to deprive human beings of their basic rights to sleep and rest and privacy. Make it cheaper and easier for a contractor to use muffled equipment than to withstand your pressures.

Make up a list of who to heckle about the noise. This will include manufacturers, distributors (stores, etc.), civic organizations, politicians. If the noise source is a brand name product, look up the name of the corporation president (your library can help you). Write to him. Send him petitions. Let the press know of your action. Do the same if the problem is one of government irresponsibility. The names of city officials will also be available in your library. The League of Women Voters can be helpful in identifying elected officials on all levels of government.

Any or all of the above measures are justifiable. Nonetheless, some can lead to arrest. This must be expected and accepted. The courts, however, should recognize the differences between destructive protests and protests of social value.

If workers want to preserve their hearing and general health, they may have to take similar steps. They must find a doctor brave enough and compassionate enough to start the battle for less occupational noise. Workers should demand that their unions press for work environments that minimize hearing damage and extra-auditory stress.

Since most of the burden for noise control is thrown on local government, there should be equivalents of "Nader's Raiders" to investigate the operations of city government from the mayor's office on down. These investigations will determine the legal or declared responsibility of each agency, and check its track record. This type of investigation will uncover little omissions, such as the omission of a municipality to have the decibel machinery necessary to back up a zoning resolution. It will also lead to the possibility of lawsuits against mayors and police and license and other commissioners for failing to act according to the rules.

If for whatever reason you cannot take overt action, don't give yourself an ulcer. Make photographs of the noisemaker and the noise source and throw darts at them. Or make up your own "coloring book":

This is the Smith Family. They've lived in noisy cities all their lives. They don't mind—anymore. They are deaf now. They can't hear music, birds chirping, the wind in the trees.

They can barely hear speech. Color them a sad color.

This is a bureaucrat.

He awards contracts. He doesn't bother to include "quiet" specifications. He lives where it is quiet.

When he leaves government, he hopes to work for the noise-maker. Color his heart indifferent gray.

Once people become committed to fighting noise, the question of goals must come up. There is no absolute answer, no inflexible decibel level to permit. Nevertheless, between the current acoustic anarchy and the ideal, there is room for an initial step that offers better than a modicum of protection. Somehow or other we managed to select that first highway speed limit, modifying it with experience.

In 1966, after Baden-Baden noise congress, I had the opportunity to be the guest of an eminent European acoustician, a man responsible for some of the most progressive noise criteria on the Continent. I had a question for him.

"How do you arrive at decibel levels for your noise laws? "

This great scientist, who is also a great humanitarian, looked at me with a twinkle in his eye, and replied: "I pick a number."

He quickly continued when he saw my startled reaction.

"Yes, I pick a number. Once we have a starting level, through experience, from the reaction of the noisemakers and the public, we can make the necessary revisions. I have been using this system for many years, and not only has it worked for my country, my criteria are used as the basis for similar legislation in other countries in Europe."

A thoughtful society acts to provide at the very least an environment which is aurally comfortable, free of excessive annoyance and physiological harm. There should be an immediate goal of protecting the sleep of all, but certainly the ill, the aged, the mother and child at home. There must be "oases of quiet." Night workers who sleep during the day need a quiet bedroom.

Concern for privacy is a manifestation of a relatively sophisticated, thoughtful society. Primitive man and people living under dictatorships fail to enjoy privacy. (The dictator, of course, is surrounded by privacy.) Home must provide more than shelter from rain and cold. The right to privacy, rest, and sleep must not be left to the discretion of Pan Am, GM, and the neighbors.

From mankind's point of view all machines to which human beings are exposed should be designed for quiet operation. All enclosures in which humans live, work, or play must be designed —or redesigned—to keep out noise intrusion.

Stated as a set of principles, the goal of noise abatement is:

1. The man-made environment is to be adapted to the needs of living creatures, not the reverse.
2. Human considerations are to come before economic considerations.
3. Noise exposure is to be in moderation. Undue stress on physiological and psychological processes is not to be tolerated.
4. Machines, like well-mannered children and servants, are to be seen and not heard.
5. Noise abatement is to be recognized as an ideal, a point of orientation in decision-making. Like democracy, the ideal may never be achievable, but it helps create a framework in which society can function for the best interests of man as a social and political animal.

Once noise abatement *in the human interest* is adopted as policy, the details will fall into place. The first step in that direction is to erase all preconceived notions of who is responsible for what, and the narrow view that only specialists have the basic answers to human problems. The President of the United States should appoint a blue-ribbon panel to investigate the entire sphere of occupational noise, its members not connected in any way with industry or the military. We must put an end to the tyranny of the "expert" as the man who sets all the rules. It is for the public to determine the goals for a quieter environment.

The Federal government should convene a National Congress of Parties of Interest. The three elements of this Congress would be government, the public, and commerce and industry.

After basic preparation, each of the three groups should convene separately to hammer out the details. Government, on its part, should convene a National Congress of Governments.

At this meeting the three levels of government—local, state, and Federal—would thrash out an over-all program for noise abatement. The details of guidelines, codes, enforcement and research needs would be spelled out and a plan evolved for providing all government units with the necessary testing facilities without unnecessary duplication. A permanent Intergovernment Noise Abatement Council would be established to act as liaison within government, and to represent government at the final Congress of Parties of Interest.

At this ultimate Congress all should agree on and adopt a Noise Index. To arrive at this Index, an arbitrary baseline would be developed from an analysis of noise in the natural environment. To this "ideal" would be added the increments to account for the unavoidable, and the desirable sounds of living and working together. No sound-producing product or piece of equipment would be allowed into the environment which could destroy the intent of these guidelines. In evaluating the noise emission of a given product, account would be taken of the other noise emissions that would co-exist with the product in question. It makes no sense to set a given decibel limit for a single motor vehicle without acknowledging that a highway or a city will be exposed to millions of such vehicles.

No machine should be permitted that as a normal function of its operation destroys sleep, the ability to converse, or rest, or that causes repeated abnormal physiological changes within the body. Common sense will be necessary. A machine that will not operate during the night will not have to be as quiet; by the same token, a machine that operates both day and night will have to be designed to operate as if it always operated at night.

Once government assigns a top priority to noise abatement it must establish a noise abatement function with the responsibility and the authority to oversee all government planning and actions that modify the noise environment. At the present time the various existing agencies are jockeying for control of this field.

Fearful of the powers of a central agency, some would prefer to keep noise abatement as a fragmented operation of government. Is it logical to give the responsibility for eliminating hovercraft noise to the FAA if the craft operate 18 inches above the ground, and to the state police if they operate closer to the ground, and to the marine agencies if they operate above water? The Federal Council for Science and Technology recommends there be no central mechanism.

But today there is no instrument of government on any level capable of performing an effective noise abatement function. The answer may be a Department of Ecology. But this remains to be developed after the new ecology is clearly defined, and the definition includes man in his artificial environments, as well as man in relation to grass, trees, insects, and mountains.

For the immediate future, the Public Health Service offers one practical answer. It has a pilot program to learn from: the National Air Pollution Control Administration, an agency of the Consumer Protection and Environmental Health administration of the Department of Health, Education, and Welfare.

A pro-people noise abatement program will be so radical, it will be necessary to train a new corps of noise control experts. We are going to have to teach our engineers the principles of design for quiet. It was a shock—and the world of noise abatement is one shock after another—to discover that engineers are not being taught the elements of noise control.

We are going to have to teach noise abatement in the technical high schools. At the present time noise control is limited to graduate students, either in physics or in engineering. For basic urban monitoring and enforcement, a program on the high school level may be adequate. We turn out automobile mechanics and radio and TV repairmen in our high schools; there is no reason why we cannot train noise control technicians at that level. The Zurich Police Office of Noise Control is staffed by men who have received one year of noise-abatement instruction at the *hochschulle*. To meet the needs of everyday noise abatement we will need thousands of technicians, far more than the handful of men exposed to noise training in graduate courses or in the defense and space programs.

Courses of instruction will include traditional decibel techniques, plus lectures on the purpose of man and government, the social sources of noise, and the ecological consequences; lectures by independent medical and other researchers on the extra-auditory as well as the auditory effects of noise—and more.

Regulatory officials, planners, department heads, highway design and transportation officials should graduate from this program with a belief that the city should not remain what Lewis Mumford calls a "tyrannapolis."' An esprit de corps should be developed in this student body, a sense of dedication to a cause almost as exciting as space exploration, and much more difficult to pursue.

Once dispersed to their duties, the men working in the government sector should be encouraged in their loyalty to the novel objective of putting people first. Regulations should be established to remove any potential for conflict-of-interest between top policymaking members of regulatory bodies and the industries they regulate.

A corps of noise abatement specialists with a zeal for their work will reduce the need for detailed legislation. They will find it possible to quiet the noisemaker in the absence of a specific law, and to enforce noise abatement law without fireworks. In their attitude of partnership for maximum tranquility, these men must think of themselves as educators in a new field, not as police.

To hear what's going on, all levels of government should institute some form of noise monitoring.

If the chief sources of excessive noise, such as aircraft, cannot be designed to operate quietly for another fifteen years or so, we must restrict the number of intrusions. Psychoacousticians tell us that annoyance from aircraft noise is the result of a combination of the amount of noise and the number of exposures. The number of flights, especially in the critical early morning and evening hours, must be curtailed. The new airbuses make this economically feasible—if the aviation industry is not permitted to continue to schedule the same number of flights per day as it does with the smaller aircraft.

If the automotive industry forces us to live with existing truck levels, then we have no choice but to reduce motor vehicle speeds on highways adjacent to residential and other noise-sensitive areas.

If the construction industry drags its feet, the operating hours for noisy equipment should be reduced each year until the ban is complete. Let *industry* adjust to "acceptability" criteria for a change, and we will discover that it prefers to design quieter products.

The Federal government should provide adequate in-house testing facilities. It should fund the expensive laboratories needed by the universities if they are to contribute to developments in architectural and engineering noise control. These research facilities will make it realistic for the scientist to work in the public interest without economic sacrifice. It is unrealistic to expect noise experts to serve as the social conscience of the noisemaker if his contracts are their main source of livelihood.

The human response to noise should be investigated in its totality. We must expand surveys beyond personality and economic class inputs. The absurdity of designing lawn mowers of different noise levels for different levels of income and education should be eliminated.

We must develop a mechanism for evaluating the immediate and long-range impact of innovation. We must, for example, understand the mechanisms by which amplified music turns people on. Can we define a pleasure-level which will permit the desired effect of euphoria or frenzy without hearing damage?

We must perform multi-mix research to determine the effect of noise when other stresses are present. It is one thing to be exposed to noise in the tranquility of a testing lab, and another to be exposed to the same noise in home or office.

Such research requires teams of multi-disciplinary specialists. We must augment the work of the acoustician and the ear doctor with that of the heart doctor, the neurologist, the psychiatrist. Sociologists, anthropologists, artists and philosophers should be working with engineers to define the ideal acoustic environment.

If we are to humanize the cost/benefit ratio, we must know the facts of the costs of noise control and the social and other costs of excessive noise. It should no longer be possible for an educated and respected acoustician to tell me with a straight face that to go beyond the state-of-the-art will bankrupt the nation.

If studies show that a given industry cannot afford noise reduction, and the product is necessary, there is no reason why the principle of subsidy couldn't be applied. We subsidize industry for national security. Why not for human security?

In Dr. Vogt's words: " . . . We are a practical people and prone to demand that if a thing does not have a cash value it should at least be 'good' for something. What is a sunset good for? . . . Or the ringing of tiny bells beneath the ice of a January brook? The quiet of a remote forest when even the insects are still? Isn't it a sufficient good that they delight a man's eye, and nose and ear, quiet the spirit and stretch the mind?"

A race that has learned to kill silently, can and must learn to build silently. Man must become ashamed of the primitive techniques he uses to shape, break, and rotate physical objects.

The research of NASA and DOD should be culled for civilian use. That silent submarine engine belongs in our garbage trucks as well.

Research into electric and fuel-cell power sources for civilian use must be encouraged. Such research could go beyond motor vehicles, and provide quieter power plants for construction equipment.

Government should sponsor extensive research in architectural acoustics. Can buildings be shaped to avoid the canyon-like reverberations typical of streets lined with tall buildings?

Research into noise law must include questions such as whether noisemaking should be criminal or administrative law, enforced only by police, or special inspectors, or whom.

Just as we do research on what kind of punishment will be a deterrent to crime, we need research on what kind of punishment will deter the crime of noise. Small fines may encourage the noisemaker to continue polluting. Large fines may keep sympathetic judges from convicting. The ideal enforcement provision is the power to close down a noisy operation until proper noise controls are instituted. This can be done with construction noise in Germany and in Switzerland. The Zurich police told me that in some cases construction work was stopped for as much as two weeks until the contractor came up with the required noise reduction.

It might be productive to explore forms of ostracism. Construction companies should be required to post signs saying something like "This noise may be injurious to susceptible people. It is probably making our workers deaf. But it is legal. If you don't like it, move." At the bottom of this copy should be the name and address of the company's top executive.

Convicted horn honkers should be required to adorn their cars with a warning sticker: "I drive with my horn instead of my head." Horn tooters could lose the use of their cars for one week or more.

One thought for education horn honking drivers is the setting of "horn traps." These should be set up at night in locations where horn honking is a constant irritant. Volunteers should cooperate with the police to serve as witnesses. A floodlight system should be arranged at a given corner. When the horn honking starts, on go the lights and the volunteers serve as witnesses while the police write the tickets. For more effective enforcement, the muffler and horn-blowing provisions should be taken out of the overcrowded courts and placed in special administrative courts.

All cities should be encouraged to adopt a model anti-horn code to be promulgated by the Department of Transportation. Warning signs should be posted on city sidewalks and at all entrances to a city, such as bridge toll stations and main arteries. All beginning drivers and those who write in for license renewal should be given a copy of the horn (and muffler) law. Safety testing stations should be able to test horn emissions to see they do not exceed set criteria.

As for sirens, we must address ourselves to that balance of equities which requires that thousands be disturbed in the pursuit of errands of mercy. Are more lives taken by speeding fire apparatus, police cars, and ambulances than are saved by this practice?

Truck drivers and motorcyclists must be studied. If they do gut out mufflers because they believe that a lack of intense noise denotes a lack of power, the public has a right to know. Our enforcement agencies must learn how to convert the superstitious driver to orthodox respect for quieter operation.

A center-city V/STOLport should not be created without a thorough investigation by all parties at interest, not only government agencies working for the vested interests. The burden of proof of environmental compatibility must be on the promoter. It should not be necessary for the public to scrounge for evidence of a potential hazard. Potential polluters should be required to post a performance bond guaranteeing that noise levels in homes, schools, and hospitals will not be exceeded, and that should the ambient noise level be reduced and his aircraft noise emissions stick out like a sore thumb, they too will be reduced.

The public hearings for heliports and other major innovations are usually like lynch law, the decision made in advance and the victim hanged promptly after the "due process." Provision must be made for expert input from a noise abatement agency, and for cross-examination by all parties of interest. There is nothing more frustrating, and nothing that worse serves a democracy, than to listen to publicly made misstatements without being in a position to refute them publicly.

I do not believe in retreat, but the least that should be expected is that all enclosed spaces be soundproofed at the promoter's, or if a public necessity, the government's, expense. Innocent victoms of "legal" noises must be indemnified for any and all costs. This principle will speed up the process of discovering and applying noise control to transportation and construction.

Just as the law now requires landlords to provide a minimum of thermal protection, so it must require that tenants receive needed acoustic protection. Enjoyment of property must also include the right to make noise. This means that dwellings must be built to contain sound. Instead of a "quiet" room as some suggest, why not a "noisy" room, where one can make noise to one's heart's content? The design would be the same as for the "quiet" room, but the whole concept would be a new dimension in civilized living.

The "quiet enjoyment" clause should be interpreted to mean that all living space shall be noise-rated. An apartment without adequate provisions for noise insulation would be rated second class, and its rent would not be as high as that of a first class apartment.

Building owners or operators whose tenants are exposed to a long-term disturbing noise after a lease is signed would be held responsible for maintaining that "quiet enjoyment" clause. They would be required to install soundproofed windows if necessary, and air conditioning if it became necessary to keep windows shut. If they failed to maintain a tranquil apartment they would be required to reduce the rent during the period of noise intrusion. If a tenant is forced to move, he should be reimbursed for the cost of moving, including the cost of looking for a new apartment.

In other words, a landlord should have an economic stake in

preventing new noise sources from polluting the community.

The landlord, in turn, whould be reimbursed by the private or government agency responsible for the noise. This reimbursement could be in the form of a tax reduction, or a fixed sum of money for each month of the noise intrusion.

The principle that the polluter must pay needs to become part and parcel of public policy. Already it has backing ranging from the prestigious President's Science Advisory Committee to *Life* Magazine. *Life* editorialized that the businessman should not expect someone else to clean up or live with the refuse he creates. Noise is a waste product, and the polluter should be responsible for maintaining the acoustic quality of a given environment, or at the very least soundproofing the structure he is invading.

When I protested the money the United States and the Soviet Union are pouring into space exploration, a well-read, intelligent executive explained to me that nations must express the need to compete, and that mankind is much better off if that need is expressed in trying to get to the planets first rather than on the battlefield. Fine. Let us introduce this sense of competitiveness into the environmental arena. In 1966 I suggested to the IVth International Congress for Noise Abatement that the various nations form a Decibel Olympics. A competition would be held to determine who has developed the least polluting construction techniques, transportation modes, appliances, and so forth. Awards and bonuses from both private and governmental sources should be plentiful.

This Olympics would include other than physical objects. One section would be devoted to the best in noise laws and regulations, industrial standards, legal concepts, public relations, and educational techniques.

As I write this I am thinking of an elderly woman living alone in a public housing project. The tenant above her, a drummer in a rock'n'roll group, not only practices at random but stages full dress rehearsals in his home, and his downstairs neighbor has no recourse but to endure.

There are untold thousands of similar cases across the country, involving the sick as well as the elderly. They are helpless, whether in hospitals or isolated in their individual apartments or homes. It is essential for them to have somebody to turn to. Neighborhood urgency squads should be created to explore the possibilities, bring moral pressure, and at least figuratively hold the victim's hand.

Members of such a squad should include a doctor, a psychologist, a lawyer, and a clergyman. They should bring the victim's plight to the attention of the community and publicize the names of city officials who refuse to intercede. These squads could be useful in alleviating the strain when noise victims are afraid to deal directly with noisy neighbors. There is no reason why the clergymen members could not bring these noise cruelties to the attention of their congregations. Given the moribund state of today's noise laws, the well-publicized reports of such specialist squads could do much to effect change.

Women should play a key role in these urgency squads, taking the lead in ostracizing neighborhood and commercial noise-makers. Perhaps they could come up with an American version of the technique reportedly used in Swaffham in Norfolk, England, where noisy neighbors are warned that if they don't mend their ways they will be moved into an old army hut in the country without running water and electric lights.

Women should demand that the National Commission on Product Safety investigate noisy toys, and lead in a boycott of potentially harmful toys.

Women must assume part of the responsibility for noise abatement. Not only is their own well-being at stake, but the responsibility for protecting their husbands from occupational noise falls squarely on their shoulders. It is evident that government will not voluntarily move to effectively preserve even the sense of hearing. Women can help arouse public opinion against an industry that makes deafness the price of progress. The labor movement would be indebted to women if they interceded with management.

Given incentive, the human mind is inventive enough to design for quiet. The public does not have to spell out *how* quiet. It *does have to* communicate to government and to the manufacturer that it wants a quiet*er* environment. Then it would become corporate policy not to make, buy, or sell equipment above a certain noise level. Engineering and acoustical expertise plus common sense would achieve a comfortable, non-destructive environment.

Noise is not the price of progress.

Noise is not the inevitable by-product of technology.

Noise is the price you and I pay for greed and insensitivity, and our own indifference.

A quieter world is possible, if . . . *we* don't take noise for an answer.

Selected Bibliography

Selected Bibliography

There is very little in the literature of noise and its control that meets the needs of the general public. Foreign documents await authoritative translation and distribution facilities. The following books and reference materials, some of them technical and not necessarily mirroring the author's point of view, provide additional background information on the complex subject of noise and its abatement.

BOOKS

Chalupnik, James D., ed. *Transportation Noises: A Symposium on Acceptability Criteria,* University of Washington Press, Seattle, 1970.

Harris, Cyril M., ed. *Handbook of Noise Control,* McGraw-Hill Book Company, Inc., New York, 1957.

Lord, P., and Thomas, F.L. *Noise Measurement and Control,* Heywood and Company Ltd., London, England, 1963.

Paul, Samuel. *Apartments: Their Design and Development,* Reinhold Publishing Company, New York, 1967.

Peterson, Arnold P.G., and Gross, Ervin E., Jr. *Handbook of Noise Measurement,* General Radio Company, West Concord, Mass., 1967.

279

Shurcliff, William A. *S/S/T and Sonic Boom Handbook*, Ballantine Books, New York, 1970.

DOCUMENTS, PAMPHLETS, REPORTS

Aircraft Noise Problems: Hearings Before Subcommittees of the Committee on Interstate and Foreign Commerce, House of Representatives, U.S. Government Printing Office, Washington, D.C., 1963.

Bell, Alan. *Noise: An Occupational Hazard and Public Nuisance*, World Health Organization, Public Health Paper #30, Geneva, Switzerland, 1966.

Berendt, Raymond D. *et al.*, eds. *A Guide to Airborne, Impact, and Structure Borne Noise Control in Multi-Family Buildings.* (Prepared for The Federal Housing Authority of the U.S. Department of Housing and Urban Development by The National Bureau of Standards.) U.S. Government Printing Office,. Washington, D.C., 1967.

Bond, James. *Responses of Man and Lower Animals to Acoustical Stimuli*, U.S. Department of Agriculture Agricultural Research Service, Beltsville, Maryland, 1956.

Borsky, Paul N. *Community Reactions to Sonic Booms in the Oklahoma City Area*, Wright Patterson Air Force Base, Ohio, 1965. (Available from Clearinghouse for Federal Scientific and Technical Information, Sill Building, Springfield, Va., 22151)

Brown, Edward F. *et al.*, eds. *City Noise: The Report of the Commission to Study Noise in New York City and Develop Means of Abating It.* Noise Abatement Commission, Department of Health, New York, 1930.

Citizens for A Quieter City, Inc. *One Year Later: A Progress Report*, New York, 1968. (Available through Citizens for A Quieter City, Inc., Box 777, FDR Station, New York, N.Y. 10022)

Cohen, Alexander. *Location-Design Noise Control of Transportation*, National Center for Urban and Industrial Health of the U.S. Department of Health, Education and Welfare, Cincinnati, Ohio, January, 1967.

Committee on Conservation of Hearing, American Academy of Opthalmology and Otolaryngology, Subcommittee on Noise in Industry. *Guide for Conservation of Hearing in Noise*, The Academy, Los Angeles, Cal., 1964.

Coral Gables, Florida, City of. Progressive Noise Control Legislation: Ordinance Nos. 927 (1955), 1004 (1957), 1218 (1961), 1553 (1961), 1578 (1966). (Available through City Clerk, City Hall, Coral Gables, Florida)

Federal Council for Science and Technology, Committee on Environmental Quality. *Noise—Sound Without Value*, U.S. Government Printing Office, Washington, D.C., 1968.

Franken, Peter A. *Glossary of Terms Frequently Used Concerning Noise Pollution*, American Institute of Physics, New York, 1967.

Goldstein, Sidney, and Odell, Albert H. *Comments on the Problem of Jet Aircraft Noise*, The Port of New York Authority, New York, 1966.

Goodfriend, Lewis. *Community Noise Problems—Origins and Control*, Goodfriend-Ostergaard Associates, Cedar Knolls, N.J., 1969.

Hosey, Andrew D. and Powell, Charles H. *Industrial Noise: A Guide to its Evaluation*, Public Health Service Publication No. 1572, U.S. Government Printing Office, Washington, D.C., 1967.

Jet Aircraft Noise Panel, Office of Science and Technology, Executive Office of the President. *Alleviation of Jet Aircraft Noise Near Airports: A Report of the Jet Aircraft Noise Panel*, U.S. Government Printing Office, Washington, D.C., 1966.

The Law on Noise, The Noise Abatement Society, London, 1969. (Available through the Noise Abatement Society, 6 Old Bond St., London W.2 England)

Mayor's Task Force on Noise Control. *Toward A Quieter City*, New York, 1970. (Available through the New York Board of Trade, 295 Fifth Avenue, New York, N.Y. for $1.75)

National Academy of Sciences. *Committee on S/S/T-Sonic Boom. Report on Human Response to the Sonic Boom*, Washington, D.C., 1968.

National Research Council of Canada, Division of Applied Physics. *A Brief Study of a Rational Approach to Legislative Control of Noise*, Ottawa, Canada 1968.

Noise Abatement in Practice, International Association Against Noise, Zurich, Switzerland, 1966. (Available through the International Association Against Noise, Sihlstrasse 17, Zurich, Switzerland)

Noise—Final Report. Committee on the Problem of Noise, Her Majesty's Stationery Office, London, England, 1964.

Noise in Hospitals: An Acoustical Study of Noises Affecting the Patient, Public Health Service Publication No. 930-D-11, U.S. Government Printing Office, Washington, D.C., 1963.

Noise: Its Effects on Man and Machine: Hearings before the Special Investigating Subcommittee of the Committee on Science and Astronautics, U.S. Government Printing Office, Washington, 1960.

The President's Science Advisory Committee, *Restoring the Quality of Our Environment: Report of the Environmental Pollution Panel*. U.S. Government Printing Office, Washington, D.C., 1965.

Rutgers Noise Pollution Conference. *Proceedings* of the Rutgers Noise Pollution Conference, Department of Environmental Sciences, Rutgers—The State University, New Brunswick, N.J., 1968.

Thiessen, G.J. *Community Noise—Surface Transportation,* National Research Council, Ottawa, Canada, 1967.

U.S. Congress (House). *Congressional Record,* April 21, 1966, pp. 8339-8363.

U.S. Congress (Senate), *Congressional Record,* October 29, 1969, pp. E9031-E9112.

U.S. Department of Health, Education and Welfare, Task Force on Environmental Health and Related Problems. *A Strategy for a Livable Environment,* U.S. Government Printing Office, Washington, D.C., 1967.

Ward, W. Dixon, and Fricke, James E., eds. *Noise As a Public Health Hazard,* The American Speech and Hearing Association, Washington, D.C., 1969.

PERIODICALS

CF Letter: A Report on Environmental Issues from the Conservation Foundation. Vol. 1, No. 1—, April, 1966—(Subscriptions available from The Conservation Foundation, 1717 Massachusetts Avenue, N.W., Washington, D.C. 20036, at $6.00 a year.)

Bailey, Anthony. "Noise Is A Slow Agent of Death," *The New York Times Magazine,* November 23, 1969.

Baron, Robert Alex. "Abatement Problems," *Hearing and Speech News,* Vol. 35, No. 3, May, 1967.

————. "Noise and the Urban Man," *American Journal of Public Health* Vol. 58, No. 11, November, 1968.

————. "The Noise Receiver: The Citizen," *Sound and Vibration,* Vol. 3, No. 5, May, 1968.

Botsford, James H. "Using Sound Levels to Gauge Human Response to Noise," *Sound and Vibration,* Vol. 3, No. 10, October, 1969.

Citizens for a Quieter City, Inc. *Quiet!,* Vol. 1, No. 1—, Spring, 1969—(Available through Citizens for A Quieter City, Box 777, FDR Station, New York, N.Y. 10022)

Cohen, Alexander. "Noise Effects on Health, Productivity, and Well-Being," *Transactions of the New York Academy of Sciences,* Vol. 30, No. 7, May, 1968.

Dey, Frederick. "Auditory Fatigue and Predicted Permanent Hearing Defects from Rock-and-Roll Music," *New England Journal of Medicine,* February 26, 1970

Dougherty, John D. and Welsh, Oliver. "Community Noise and Hearing Loss," *New England Journal of Medicine,* October 6, 1966.

Farr, Lee E. "Medical Consequences of Environmental Home Noises," *The Journal of the American Medical Association,* Vol. 202, No. 3, October 16, 1967.

Flugrath, James M. "Modern Day Rock and Roll Music and Damage-Risk Criteria" *The Journal of the Acoustical Society of America*, Vol. 45, No. 3, 1969.

"How Today's Noise Hurts Body and Mind," *Medical World News*, June 13, 1969.

Jansen, G. "Effect of Noise on Health," *German Medical Monthly* No. 9.

————, *et al.* "Reactions to Auditory Stimuli: Comparative Studies of Subjects in Dortmund, Germany and the Mabaan Tribe in the Sudan with Urban Populations." *Archives of Otolaryngology*, Vol. 79, May-June, 1964.

Jones, Herbert H, and Oser, James L. "Farm Equipment Noise Exposure Levels," *American Industrial Hygiene Association*, Vol. 29, March-April, 1968.

Lundberg, Bo and Russell, A.E. "Super Sonic Boom: Debate of the Month on the Problem to Come When the SST's Unroll Carpets of Thunder World-Wide" *The Rotarian*, November, 1966.

Mecklin, John M. "It's Time to Turn Down All That Noise," *Fortune*, October, 1969.

"Mental Hospital Admissions and Aircraft Noise," *Lancet*, December 13, 1969 Vol. II.

"Noise of Big Cities Is Found to Cause Stress on the Heart," *Medical Tribune*, March 29, 1965.

"Noise Studies Confirm Hazard to Man, Animals" *Medical Tribune*, January 26, 1970.

Otten, Alan L. "Bang, Crash, Thump," *The Wall Street Journal*, February 12, 1970.

QP (Quiet Please). Vol 1, No. 1—, 1961—(Available through The Noise Abatement Society, 6 Old Bond Street, London W. 1 England)

"The Racket That Won't Go Away," *Business Week*, March 16, 1968.

Ramsay, W.A. "Damage to Ottawa Air Terminal Building Produced By a Sonic Boom," *Materials Research and Standards*, November, 1964.

Rintelmann, William, and Gasway, Donald. "A Survey of Hearing Conservation Programs in Representative Aerospace Industries: Prevalence of Programs and Monitoring Audiometry" *American Industrial Hygiene Journal*, Vol. 28, July-Aug., 1967.

Rosen, Samuel, "Hearing Studies in Selected Urban-Rural Populations," *Transactions of the New York Academy of Medicine*, Vol. 29, No. 1, November, 1966.

————. "Hearing Loss and Coronary Heart Disease," *Archives of Otolaryngology*, Vol. 82, September, 1965.

————. "Noise Pollution: A Need for Action," *Medical Tribune*, January 4, 1968.

————. "Presbycusis Study of a Relatively Noise–Free Population in the Sudan," *Annals of Otology, Rhinology and Laryngology* Vol. 71, No. 3, September, 1962.

"The Sound Around Us," *Roche Medical Image*, August, 1967.

Stephenson, R.J. and Vulkan, G.H. "Urban Planning Against Noise," *Official Architecture and Planning*, May, 1967.

TVASNAC "Quotes" (Town-Village Aircraft Safety and Noise Abatement Committee of Hempstead, N.Y.) Vol. 1, No. 1—, 1969—.

The UNESCO Courier: Noise Pollution Issue. July, 1967. (Available through UNESCO Publications Center, 317 East 34th Street, New York, N.Y. 10016)

"Urban Noise Control," *Columbia Journal of Law and Social Problems*, Vol. 4, No. 1, March, 1968.

Index

Index

287